WORLD BOOK

OF GREAT

INVENTIONS

*Also by Jerome S. Meyer*

THE BOOK OF AMAZING FACTS

FUN WITH MATHEMATICS

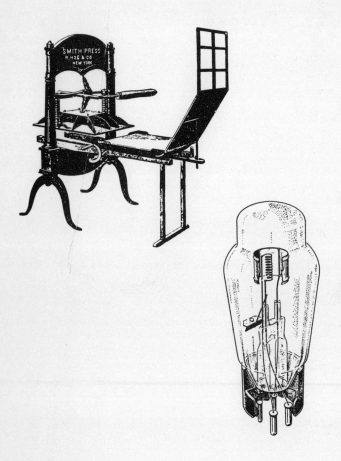

# WORLD BOOK

# OF GREAT

# INVENTIONS

BY JEROME S. MEYER

THE WORLD PUBLISHING COMPANY

CLEVELAND AND NEW YORK

LIBRARY OF CONGRESS CATALOG CARD NUMBER: 55-5290

*Copyright Acknowledgments*

Illustrations on pages 45, 61, from *Man the Maker,* by R. J. Forbes. Copyright 1950 by Abelard-Schuman, Inc.

Illustration on page 213, from *The New High Fidelity Handbook,* by Irving Greene and James Radcliffe. Revised edition copyright 1955 by Crown Publishers, Inc.

Illustration on page 57, from a wash drawing by Russell W. Porter in *Glass Giant of Palomar,* by David Woodbury. Copyright 1948 by Dodd, Mead & Company.

Illustrations on pages 19, 92, 93, 94, 104, 105, 106, from *The Turning Wheel,* by Arthur Pound. Copyright 1934 by Doubleday & Company, Inc.

Illustration of the Mark Twain letter on page 64. Copyright by Harper & Brothers, Publishers.

Illustrations on pages 96, 97, 98, from *Iron Horses,* by Edwin P. Alexander. Copyright 1941 by W. W. Norton & Company, Inc.

C W

# CONTENTS

INTRODUCTION                                                          11

I.    Primitive Man                                                   13

II.   Early Civilizations and Great Thinkers of Antiquity            18

III.  The Progress of Science and Invention in the Middle
      Ages and the Renaissance                                        29

IV.   Developments in the Mechanical Age                              38

      1. THE STORY OF PRINTING                                        38

         *The Linotype Machine*  43

         *The Early Printing Presses*  44

         *The Modern Printing Presses*  48

      2. THE STORY OF OPTICS                                          51

         *The First Lens*  51

         *Modern Optics*  53

         *The World's Largest Eye*  56

      3. THE STORY OF THE TYPEWRITER                                  59

      4. THE STORY OF THE SEWING MACHINE                              66

      5. THE STORY OF PHOTOGRAPHY                                     75

         *"Nature's Images on Silver"*  75

         *The Movies*  82

6. THE STEAM ENGINE     91

V.    The Internal Combustion Engine     100

1. THE GASOLINE ENGINE     100

2. THE STORY OF THE AUTOMOBILE     102

3. THE DIESEL ENGINE     110

4. THE STORY OF FLIGHT     110

*The Airplane*   110

*The Principle of the Airplane*   118

*Jet and Rocket Propulsion*   123

VI.    The Age of Electricity     126

1. THE DISCOVERY OF ELECTRICITY     126

2. THE STORY OF THE GENERATOR, THE MOTOR, AND THE ELECTROMAGNET     133

*The Principle of Today's Electric Generator*   138

*The Electric Motor*   141

*The Electromagnet*   145

3. THE STORY OF THE TELEGRAPH     147

*The Teletype*   158

*The Telegraph Today*   159

4. THE STORY OF THE TELEPHONE     164

*The Inventors of the Telephone*   171

*How the Telephone Works*   172

*The Dial Telephone*   173

5. THE VACUUM TUBE     181

*Edison "Missed the Boat"*   183

*Lee De Forest and the Radio Vacuum Tube*   187

*The Working Principle of Vacuum Tubes*   189

*The Photoelectric Tube*   191

6. THE STORY OF RADIO AND TELEVISION    194

    *Radio*  194

    *Television*  202

    *How Television Works*  204

7. SOME APPLICATIONS OF THE ELECTROMAGNET AND
THE VACUUM TUBE    208

    *Electrical Sound Recording*  208

    *Electrical Transcriptions*  210

    *Magnetic Tape Recording*  213

    *Sound for Moving Pictures*  215

    *Pictures That Are Sent Through Space*  216

    *The Electric Bell*  217

VII. What Does the Future Hold for Us?    219

Appendix. OTHER IMPORTANT INVENTIONS    231

What Are the Fifteen Greatest Inventions of All Time?    262

    ACKNOWLEDGMENTS    263

    INDEX    265

# INTRODUCTION

Because a French priest in the thirteenth century found that he could read an important document better by looking at it through curved glass, hundreds of millions of human lives were eventually saved. Because a nineteenth-century mechanic discovered that a piston could be moved with great force when illuminating gas was exploded inside a metal cylinder, the oceans of the world were ultimately narrowed and all nations of the earth became neighbors. Because a professor in Denmark in the early nineteenth century thought it most peculiar that the needle of his compass pointed west when brought near an electric current, every electrical invention that we have today was made possible.

Each invention, from the simplest to the most complicated, started in humble circumstances—a germ of an idea roughly penciled on a scrap of paper, later to be improved and developed by the painstaking efforts and co-operation of scientists, engineers, and technicians. How many have died without recognition will never be known. But to all of those who have toiled endlessly for the benefit of humanity we owe our everlasting gratitude, for they have contributed to the great mass of knowledge which spells longer life and greater comfort for all of us. Great names, immortal names, stand out like mountain peaks in the scientific range, yet credit is due to all who have devoted their lives to science and its practical application.

The story of great inventions, from primitive man to the Atomic Age, is one of the most fascinating ever told. It is the story of how man began to think creatively, and by means of this new experience was able over the centuries to tame fire, till the soil, fashion articles from clay and stone, discover the fundamentals of all mechanics, invent the wheel, and, best of all, record his thoughts in writing and pictures for posterity. It tells of the first civilizations and how the men of antiquity, through their resourcefulness and curiosity, pried into the secrets of nature to discover ways and means of making their lives easier. It is the story of man's fight against his own fears and superstitions, and his never-ending search for the truth and beauty in nature and nature's laws. Each age, whether it be that of the Greek or Roman cultures, the Middle Ages, or the enlightenment of the Renaissance, has its own particular fascination, but by far the greatest age of invention started with the taming of electricity. Here is man at the pinnacle of his creative genius. Who would believe that a little piece of iron and a coil of wire would run our world today? Who would ever guess that bottled vacuum would change our civilization? And who can tell today what great benefits the Atomic Age will bring tomorrow?

Yes, the story of great inventions is the story of man's victory over discouragement and adversity; it is the story of his amazing vision, tenacity, and determination to overcome all obstacles in order to improve his world.

J.S.M.

# CHAPTER I

# PRIMITIVE

# MAN

Man's transition from cave dweller to civilized man took hundreds of thousands of years. As it all happened centuries before recorded history, we cannot positively say just how and when his first discoveries were made. We can only suggest what logically might have taken place and let it go at that.

Among the first creations of man were weapons. In order to survive he had to hunt wild beasts and protect himself from his enemies. In the beginning he used large sticks and the sharp bones from dead animals, but later he discovered that stones and rocks were much more effective. They were more durable than bones and more deadly than sticks. Hurled at an enemy, they could do considerable damage, and they could also be used to crack nuts and furnish food that would otherwise be impossible to get. Centuries later, as his observation and ability to profit from experience increased, man discovered that sharpened stones not only killed more quickly, but could be used for digging the earth and preparing the ground for the planting of seeds which he had already learned would sprout and pro-

duce food. The first crude agriculture was born from this.

Of course man was aware of fire. He had seen it time and again in the burning lava from erupting volcanoes, or when a fireball from a flash of lightning ignited some dry leaves in the primeval forest. Perhaps his first thoughts were that fire was alive, since it was always moving. Perhaps, on many occasions, he tried to kill it the way he killed the wild beasts of the jungle, only to find that fire would not die in that way. Or he might have tried to make friends with it, only to suffer terrible pain from the severe burns it inflicted on him. And so he came to fear fire, and thought of it as the work of some evil spirit to be avoided whenever and wherever possible.

Now there must have been a day in that dim and distant past when one particular cave man, much braver and more intelligent than the rest, reasoned that the fire demon could be used to advantage once the demon was conquered. His limited imagination probably told him that fire could keep him and his mate warm on chilly nights, and its light would protect them from the wild beasts. Whether alone or with the help of others, this hero had courage enough to challenge the demon. He might have approached a fire with tree branches, ignited them, and carried them to his cave, where he kept the flames going by adding more wood. That unknown and unsung genius, whoever he was, was the first to make use of fire, and to him for his bravery and intelligence we owe much of what we have today. Many centuries later man learned to produce fire by rubbing a stick quickly on another piece of wood.

As time went on other uses of fire were discovered, all of them of vital importance not only to primitive man but to the foundation of our civilization. We don't know how man first discovered cooking. He might have been returning from a hunting trip with a few dead rabbits slung over his massive shoulders and, seeing the remains of a small fire in the forest, paused to rest and warm himself. It is conceivable that he accidentally dropped the rabbits into this fire, and before he could rescue them they became cooked. When he ate them he must have noticed the great difference in the flavor of the meat, and it is not unlikely that he figured out that this difference was caused by the fire. Profiting by experience, he tried putting other foods into the fire and found that they, too, were more palatable. And so, through trial and error over a long period of time, cooking was introduced to the world.

Soon after the discovery of cooking, primitive man found another use for fire. The practice of sowing seeds and eating the grain they yielded was well established by this time, but in order to keep the grain for use during the long winter months it was necessary to store it in some sort of container. He noticed that in summer the soft, damp clay hardened under the heat of the tropical sun, so he fashioned pots and bowls from it and heated them in the fire until they were thoroughly baked and hard as stone. These he used for carrying water from the stream or lake to his cave, as well as for cooking and storing grains and other foods against a time when they might become scarce. Clay containers served so many useful purposes that pottery became one of the very first industries. But though jugs and bowls and pots were excellent for carrying water, they were very heavy for carrying grain and berries; and so man, hoping to produce containers that were lighter yet just as serviceable, looked to the long grass of the fields and the twigs of the bushes for the answer. Over many decades he developed the art of weaving. Crude baskets began to appear, and weaving started a new trend of thought.

Nature had robbed him of the thick hairy protection it afforded to apes and other animals of the forest. Every time he hunted, the brambles and

*Producing fire by*
*rubbing a stick rapidly on wood*

thick underbrush tore at his bare legs and body and very often caused him serious injury. His innate creative ability told him that since the skins of the beasts protected them, they could also protect him. So he prepared animal skins for himself by scraping them with his sharp stone tools, puncturing holes in them, and tying them around his bare body with roots and grass. This not only protected him from injury and kept him warm on damp and chilly days, but it eventually enabled him to settle and live in every part of the world regardless of climate. Then the first weaving of cloth began. Gradually the tough and hardened skins of animals gave way to a loose and lighter material woven from grass.

As prehistoric man learned to use stone implements for scraping, cutting, and plowing the fields, he became attracted and fascinated by the glitter and sparkle and shine that some of the rocks possessed. So he smashed them into small bits and wore the hard shiny pieces around his neck and wrists to show himself off in peacock fashion. This was the very first jewelry in the world. There were many different-colored pieces to be found in those rocks, too, and over the years they were hammered out and worn, and great superstitions grew up about them.

But as these pieces were scarce and the shiny yellow-red stuff in the rocks was plentiful, it was only natural for man to examine the latter more closely. Occasionally this material was found in the raw state, free from its rocky prison. It was different from stone. It was heavier and more durable, and it could be bent by powerful hands into any number of different shapes.

Many decades passed, and then another thinker, probably a potter who spent most of his time hardening clay in fire, got the idea of heating the rocks that contained this shiny yellow-red material in a fire, just as he heated clay. He must have reasoned that if fire could change soft clay into a stonelike material, it might change these rocks into something different too. Acting upon this remarkable theory, he tossed some of the smaller rocks into a particularly large fire, and a seeming miracle took place! Unknown to this prehistoric thinker, the wood fire supplied the chemical process necessary to free the pure metal from the rock, and, lo, a small stream of melting copper slowly flowed out and cooled! The first metal was thus produced by man, and a new age was born. Without the slightest knowledge of chemistry, and with absolutely no conception of the process of smelting and freeing metals from their native state, primitive man, by his incredible intuition, thus laid one of the cornerstones of our present civilization.

At first man didn't appreciate the enormous value of his discovery. He heated the copper ore time and again, and made bright beads from the drippings. These he wore with colored stones and rough gems, but as soon as he found out how plentiful this shiny yellow stuff was, he began to think about using it for more important purposes. As it was more durable than stone and could be hammered easily into all kinds of shapes, he decided that it would be ideal for making spearheads and cutting tools. He then began to build hotter fires in stone ovens solely for the purpose of obtaining this metal, and it was thus that the first smelting was done in primitive furnaces constructed from hardened clay and stone. As hotter furnaces were built, other metals with higher melting points, like tin and zinc, began to flow and mix with the copper. This is when the Stone Age ended and the Bronze Age commenced.

And so the taming of fire, the use of stones as weapons and tools for digging and planting, the making of pottery, the weaving of clothing, and the discovery of metals were the first five remarkable discoveries of primitive man. But more important discoveries were yet to come, before the dawn of recorded history.

Man's first real invention, and one of the most important in history, was the wheel, which we all take for granted. All our transportation, as well as every machine in the world, from the most complicated to the simplest, is dependent upon the wheel.

The wheel is the simplest and perhaps the most remarkable of all inventions. There are no wheels in nature, and no living thing was ever created with wheels. How and when man invented it is, of course, unknown. But perhaps it came from the discovery that the carcass of a heavy animal could be transported through the forest more easily by rolling it over a number of logs than by carrying it. As time went on, man realized that while it was much easier to roll heavy loads on logs than to carry them, the logs themselves weighed a lot, too, so why not cut down on their

weight? It must have taken some great prehistoric thinker whose imagination was far superior to the others to picture in his mind two thin slices of log connected at their centers by a strong stick. This undoubtedly would roll along just as the logs did, yet would be much lighter and easier to handle. It was then that the wheel and axle came into existence, and with them came the first primitive carts, which were to be developed into the chariots of ancient Rome many centuries later.

With the invention of the wheel and the first crude carts came the further domestication of animals and a great increase in travel. So it was necessary to clear pathways, or what amounted to very primitive roads.

A comparatively short time before the beginning of recorded history, man discovered the principle of the lever, the second in the quartet of the basic elements of all the machinery in existence. While the wheel was perfect for moving heavy loads along the ground, it was useless at that time for lifting very heavy weights. It was found that a rock—too heavy to be lifted by one man—could be moved, and even lifted, by placing one end of a strong tree branch under it. The body of the branch was then passed over a log close to the rock, the other end projecting freely into the air, as shown here. Now a man hanging on to this free end of the branch found that as his weight forced it down the heavy rock at the other end was lifted slightly off the ground, something that had never been accomplished before. So important was this feat of strength to prehistoric man that he did a considerable amount of experimenting to

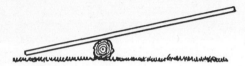

*The first crude lever was
a long stick laid over a log*

find out its whys and wherefores. He tried lifting other rocks with shorter branches and failed. Then he tried longer branches and discovered that the longer the branch and the nearer the fallen trunk to the rock, the better he was able to lift it. He also observed that in lifting the rock a short distance his end of the branch had to be pulled down a long distance.

Prehistoric man, with his amazing resourcefulness, gradually learned to tame the forces of nature and use them to his own advantage. His discoveries and inventions up to a little before the dawn of history, some 10,000 years ago, still stand as the foundations of our present civilization. One of his last inventions was the one that transformed him from a savage to a civilized human being. He had discovered not only how to think but how to record his thoughts, so that others might know them and profit by them. Starting as far back in time as the taming of fire, he cut crude, childlike picture diagrams on rocks to indicate certain specific events. From these came the very early Egyptian hieroglyphics, which later appeared on papyrus. It was the invention of papyrus, the ancestor of paper, that was of great importance.

The marrow from the papyrus stalk was extracted and cut into thin strips which were placed side by side, forming the basis for a second set of parallel strips which was glued over the first layer and at right angles to it. The sheet was then dried in the sun and beaten smooth with mallets. On the finished papyrus the ancient Egyptians wrote with the ancestors of our pen and ink: a thin sharp stick dipped in the juice of certain berries.

Some centuries later papyrus was faced with a very strong competitor, which ultimately became the standard writing material of antiquity. This was the skin of donkeys or sheep, which had been specially treated, cleared of hair, stretched, and smoothed. It came from the ancient town of Pergamum in Asia Minor and was called parchment.

# CHAPTER II

# EARLY CIVILIZATIONS AND GREAT THINKERS OF ANTIQUITY

Some of the first civilized peoples lived about 6,000 years ago in the valley of the Nile. Hieroglyphics carved on stone, statues, paintings, art treasures, documents on papyrus, and hundreds of other relics have provided us with a valuable insight into the customs, culture, and religious beliefs of these human beings.

Just how much the ancient Egyptians knew about science is still a mystery. Perhaps, in years to come, Egyptologists will unearth records that throw a new light on the subject, but at present all we know is that their scientific knowledge was limited. They knew little or nothing about machinery, and, while they measured time by the sun and had a workable calendar, they seem to have been unaware of planets or planetary motion, nor could they predict any celestial event.

In mathematics they were more advanced. They could add and subtract with ease, although their method of number notation was crude and cumbersome (for example, to write the number 99, an Egyptian had to inscribe twenty-seven signs and symbols).

Inventive science was almost unknown in ancient Egypt. The vast majority did not seek to discover scientific laws. The Nile river was their universe; all life depended upon it. It made the surrounding country fertile and enabled the people to sow grain and reap fine harvests year after year. Wherever it flowed, plant and animal life were plentiful, but in the vast area to the northwest all was desert. It is no wonder, then, that the early Egyptians, not understanding how a river can promote life, believed it to be a god to be worshiped just the way other gods were. They pictured the Nile God as a fat, elderly man, and they built statues and offered sacrifices to him in order to invoke good harvests and ensure their safety against floods and famine.

The great deserts of the north and west literally imprisoned the people in the fertile Nile valley. All their traveling was done in boats on that river, so that a long trip was always

*An early Egyptian wheel*

associated with a boat. Being extremely religious, the reigning kings were convinced that they would travel to heaven after death to join the Sun God in his daily trips across the sky and follow him in his passage through the dark underworld every night. Buried in the great tombs of the Pharaohs were ships with long oars to enable the immortals to accompany the dead king on his journey to the Sun God.

Obviously people with such beliefs were not very scientific, yet they were the same people who, with only a smattering of mathematics, built the great pyramids which housed the remains of the Pharaohs and which still stand, after 5,000 years, as one of the wonders of the ancient world.

The pyramids were built without machinery. The huge stones were put into place with the aid of wedges and a heavy wooden crowbar acting as a lever. They were rolled on wooden rollers and hauled from the river by rope, each stone requiring a dozen or more slaves. There are no records of a pulley or block and tackle, the lifting being done solely by hauling and pushing the stones up ramps. The tools used consisted of large saws about eight feet long, copper chisels, wooden molds for making bricks, tubular drills for boring, and plaster for filling in the holes and gaps between the stones. The building of such a colossal structure with such crude and scanty equipment may seem impossible, but when you consider that the undertaking required about 100,000 slaves who toiled for twenty years, you will understand how it was accomplished. As there were thousands and thousands of slaves always available and no need for hurry, labor-saving machinery would have been entirely unnecessary.

But it takes more than 100,000 slaves and twenty years to build a pyramid. Some working knowledge of structural design is essential, and the job has to be planned just as any other engineering job. Plans of the pyramids exist today. One of them, drawn on papyrus, is in the Turin Museum and another, on limestone, is in the Museum in Cairo. But we don't know for sure how much knowledge the engineers of the pyramids had when they started to build them. It is very likely that they gained knowledge as they went along. In twenty years one can learn a great deal by observation, experiment, and experience. It is entirely possible that the ancient engineers made plenty of errors at first. A false calculation, a falling stone, a few dead slaves—it was of little consequence. It was charged up to experience and went into the list of things *not* to do. Profiting by past errors, the Egyptian engineers must have kept careful records and handed

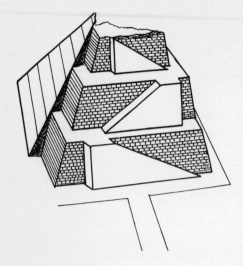

This cut-away drawing shows the construction of the pyramid. The huge stones were rolled on logs or rollers up the ramps and put into place by hundreds of slaves. There is no record of pulleys being used at this time.

them down from one generation to the next. If these records exist they will undoubtedly be unearthed at some future time.

The Great Pyramid at Gizeh (the largest of three), built for King Cheops about 5,000 years ago, has a base 746 feet square and rises to a height of 476 feet. If this massive tomb were placed in New York it would cover nine square blocks and be more than forty stories high. So perfectly do the blocks fit together and so carefully are the joints concealed that one might think the structure was one huge chunk of stone.

Just as amazing as the actual building of the pyramids was the organization of the work. Millions of bricks had to be made and put into the inner wall and more than two million huge limestone blocks had to be cut and floated on boats down the Nile and hauled up numerous ramps and placed in their proper locations. The cutting had to be figured out accurately in advance, and the mathematics used certainly involved geometry, although this was many centuries before Euclid. Each huge stone was marked with the date, the number, the place where it was to fit, and the name of the gang of quarrymen working on that particular job. The hundred thousand workers were divided into three groups. About 30,000 did the quarrying, cutting, and shipping, about 40,000 built the brick inner walls and hauled the big stones on rollers from the boats up the ramps to their proper places and set them with mathematical precision, while the remaining 30,000 workers supplied food and shelter for these builders.

With all their remarkable cleverness and skill, the ancient Egyptians never learned to think scientifically. There were no theoretical scientists in Egypt at that time. The people believed that everything in nature was molded and placed there by the various gods on the day of creation, and it was not for mortals to interfere. To try to find out the whys and wherefores of nature was sure to invoke the wrath of the gods and bring on floods and famine.

The lack of interest in scientific theory characterized the period between the end of the Stone Age and the beginning of Greek culture. In the thousand years from 600 B.C. to 400 A.D., the ancients made great strides. Philosophy developed and flowered into the first scientific thinking. The philosophers of ancient Greece spent most of their time inquiring into the nature of the universe. What is matter? What makes some things hard and tough and other things soft and loose? What is heat? Where did all the water in the ocean come from? These and hundreds of other questions were asked and partially answered by the Greek philosophers.

The Greeks were the first theoretical scientists, but unfortunately their theories and observations lacked the necessary instruments and equipment to verify them. Application of theory was almost unknown. The world's great inventions have resulted from applying theory and observation for practical use. Maxwell's electromagnetic theory revolutionized scientific thought in the middle of the nineteenth century, but it would have remained just a great and incomprehensible document if men like Hertz, Tesla, Lodge, Marconi, Fleming, De Forest, and others had not studied it and gradually put it to practical use to give the world radio, radar, wireless telegraphy, and television. Einstein's investigation of matter and energy and his famous equation $E = mc^2$, after careful study by practical scientists and engineers, opened the new era of atomic science. When asked about the value of his last and most difficult field theory, the scientist answered, "Come back and see me in twenty years."

The ancient Greeks considered theory all-important and its practical application childish and of little consequence. Theoretical science was called philosophy; invention was considered degrading. Like Egypt, Greece had millions of slaves to do the work, and the Greek scientists saw no reason to waste valuable philosophical thinking on such a practical down-to-earth thing as labor-saving machinery. It is likely that they could have invented a great many useful machines if they had wanted to. They had the knowledge and the know-how and were well acquainted with the working principles of the lever, the wedge, the wheel and axle, and the screw.

But it is perhaps just as well that the philosophers of ancient Greece had this attitude. Out of theory grows invention, and their ability to think scientifically and their numerous contributions to the field of mathematics furnished the basic elements of all inventive science which followed them.

Ancient Greece produced some of the greatest scientists, philosophers, and mathematicians the world has ever known. Among the immortals of antiquity we find such names as Aristotle, Pythagoras, Plato, Archimedes, Hero, Euclid, and dozens of others. These men, and many others, laid the very foundations of physics and chemistry and mathematics and furnished the basic elements of all inventions. Mathematics, the language of science, is also the language of invention. If it can be classed as an invention, then Pythagoras was one of its chief inventors. Some historians credit him with being the "inventor" of arithmetic, and his incredible achievements seem to verify that statement. He defined and classified numbers as odd, even, prime, square, triangular, and composite. An accomplished musician of his time, he discovered that musical intervals correspond with certain definite arithmetical ratios based upon the lengths of the vibrating strings.

To enumerate the achievements of the Greek philosophers and scientists is beyond the scope of a book that deals primarily with inventions. Two names, however, stand out above all the others in the field of invention and practical application of theory. One was Archimedes.

Archimedes, the "Einstein of Antiquity," was the first human being to apply the principle of the screw and pulley to practical use, and he can be correctly called the "inventor" of these two vitally important machines.

Archimedes was born in Syracuse, Sicily, about 287 B.C. His entire life, from boyhood to the time he was killed by a Roman soldier, at the age of seventy-five, was spent in rigorous mathematical research, and, while he is generally known for his studies of floating bodies, his major works deal with parabolas, conchoids, spirals, and conic sections and are so difficult that only an experienced mathematician can understand them.

So keen was his mind and his imagination that it is generally believed he had the basic idea of the calculus, which was not invented until nineteen centuries later by Newton and Leibnitz. David Eugene Smith, in a foreword to *A Treatise on Archimedes,*

*Archimedes: from a painting by Niccolò Baradino*

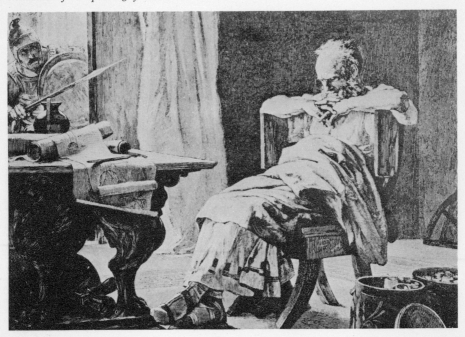

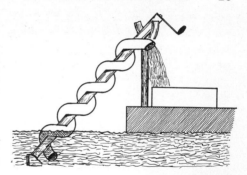

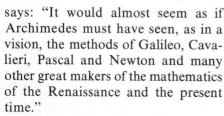

*The Archimedean screw, used to raise water from a lower to a higher level. Note the crank, which was not used in machinery until centuries later*

says: "It would almost seem as if Archimedes must have seen, as in a vision, the methods of Galileo, Cavalieri, Pascal and Newton and many other great makers of the mathematics of the Renaissance and the present time."

Archimedes, in addition to being the Einstein of antiquity, possessed the mechanical genius of a Leonardo da Vinci. His inventions were extremely important, but he looked down on them as mere amusements in geometry, worked out in compliance with King Hero's request to apply some of his genius to practical things. Here are a few instances of how he obeyed the king's instructions.

Upon investigation of the laws of the lever, Archimedes made his famous statement, "Give me a place to stand, and I will move the earth." The king, struck with amazement at this statement from such an eminent scientist, asked Archimedes to make good his boast to a very limited degree by moving an enormously heavy weight with little effort. He suggested moving one of his large ships from its dock without the necessary assistance of hundreds of men. Archimedes, through a system of compound and movable pulleys which he invented, succeeded in moving the ship loaded with men and cargo, smoothly and evenly, merely by sitting comfortably in a chair nearby and pulling a few ropes.

Another instance of the practical application of Archimedes' genius: It was anticipated that the siege of Syracuse by the Romans would last only a few months. Instead, Archimedes' "engines" of destruction held back the enemy for three years. So harmful were these giant slingshots that hurled darts and rocks at the enemy's ships, that Marcellus, a Roman general second only to the Julius Caesar who followed him, remarked: "What, must we give up fighting with this geometrical Briareus, who plays pitch-and-toss with our ships, and, with a multitude of darts which he showers at a single moment upon us, really outdoes the hundred-hand giants of mythology?" Certainly no higher tribute to Archimedes could have been paid.

Archimedes' insatiable thirst for geometrical truths produced a number of books on planes, spheres, cylinders, and spirals. In this last subject the great mathematician was at his best, and it was probably his application of the spiral to a practical problem that brought to light one of the most important and fundamental principles of all machinery—the screw. The king asked Archimedes to lift water from the hold of a ship, without human aid and purely by mechanical means. To do this the scientist invented the Archimedean screw. If you stop to consider all the applications of the screw in our modern machinery, you will agree that Archimedes deserves a place among the immortals of science.

About sixty years after the death of Archimedes, Hero of Alexandria was born. Nobody knows the exact date of his birth, but, according to the best authorities, he lived about 150 B.C. In addition to being a great mathematician, Hero invented the siphon, the gearwheel, the pump, the water clock (the ancestor of our present clocks), and the steam engine.

His treatise on mechanics, translated into Arabic, was well preserved and carefully studied by mechanics and engineers of the sixteenth century.

In this remarkable book of antiquity Hero lists and describes five simple ways by which an unusually heavy weight may be lifted and moved with minimum effort. These five principles form the basis of all the machinery in the world today and, though described in detail by Hero, their practical application to machinery was not to come about for more than a thousand years. They are: 1. The lever. 2. The wheel and axle. 3. The pulley. 4. The wedge. 5. The screw. While it is true that the invention of the screw is attributed to Archimedes and the wedge and the lever were known long before Hero's time, he was the man who showed for the first time that all machinery is based on these five important principles, and how to apply these principles to machinery—such as it was in those early times.

Oddly enough, neither he nor anyone else of his time realized the importance of these inventions or gave them a second's thought. Hero's book

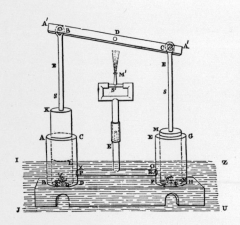

Hero's "fire engine"

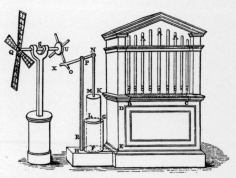

Hero's "altar organ blown by the agency of a windmill"

on pneumatics, translated into Italian in 1549 and later into English, described more than seventy totally useless inventions, most of which embody important basic principles. They were all odd-looking gadgets of the kind one might expect to see in an exhibit of magic, and their main function was to entertain and amuse. The siphon that is essential to modern plumbing and sanitation, Hero saw as a sort of toy. Nineteen centuries later, Robert Fulton would employ the power of steam for locomotion, but Hero used it to cause a little replica of a rattlesnake to make a hissing sound. He discovered the pump, so vital to our civilization, but he used it only to sound a little toy trumpet in the hands of an automaton. Among his other inventions we find a penny-in-the-slot machine for dispensing holy water, temple doors that opened when fire was lit on an altar, and methods of serving wine and water from the same bottle. It is doubtful whether any other inventor in history applied so many world-shaking ideas to what would appear to us as entertainments, but all this was in keeping with the Greek reverence for philosophy and scientific theory and indifference to practical application. Only in the case of implements of war did the Greeks apply their theoretical knowledge.

The illustrations show a number of Hero's remarkable inventions. If you overlook their amusing applications you will recognize in them the basic elements of all the machinery and many of the important inventions that were to follow centuries later.

Hero was also the inventor of the pump on the opposite page. Note in this diagram the fundamental principle on which all pumps operate. The importance of pumps in industry was not realized until the middle of the sixteenth century, sixteen hundred years after the death of the inventor. Hero applied this principle to the

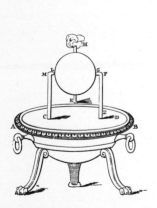

*Hero's "steam engine" which was not an engine at all but which first showed the power of steam*

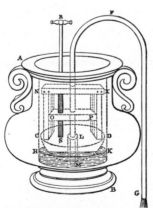

*Hero's "siphon capable of discharging a greater or less quantity of liquid with uniformity"*

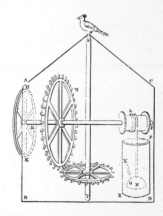

*Hero's "shrine over which a bird may be made to revolve and sing by worshipers turning a wheel"*

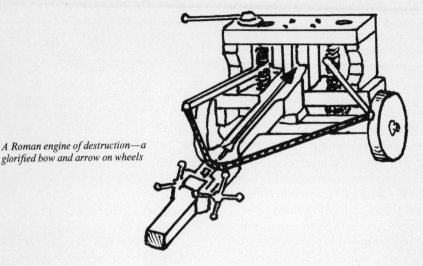

*A Roman engine of destruction—a glorified bow and arrow on wheels*

automatic pumping of an organ where the air was supplied by a wheel turning in the wind (page 24).

The ancient Romans in general were a practical people who cared less about philosophy and mathematics than did the Greeks. The Roman engineers and architects were the best in antiquity. While they were acquainted with the smelting of iron ore and were able to produce iron, they used it mainly for spears, swords, and shields, rather than in building construction. They were brilliant students of Greek geometry and trigonometry, applying their knowledge to the construction of fine bridges, roads, aqueducts, and public buildings. They accomplished practical wonders but did little theoretical scientific thinking. Because of their frequent wars, many of the inventions of the Romans were improvements on the Greek engines of destruction.

There are two reasons for the strange attitude of the Romans toward philosophy and pure mathematics. First, they were apparently too busy conquering nearby nations and forming them into their rapidly growing empire to waste much time on abstract thinking. Second, they were under a great handicap with their numerical system. Take a pencil and paper and try to multiply XI by LVII, or divide CXLIII by IX and see how you come out. It simply cannot be done with pencil and paper. The Romans did all their arithmetic on a device known as an abacus, which was the ancients' equivalent of our computing machine.

The Roman abacus was a metal plate with seven long vertical grooves and seven short grooves above them, as shown in the illustration. A number of vertical grooves of varying sizes were at the right for doing fractions. Each long groove carried four stone buttons representing units, tens, hundreds, etc., according to the particular groove, and a single stone in each of the short grooves to represent five of the units, tens, etc., in the long groove below it. By moving these little stone buttons up and down in various ways the Romans could add, subtract, multiply, and divide, as well as do fractions and decimals. The Latin word for stone is *calculus,* and the moving of these little stone buttons in the process of figuring was to *calculate.* Roman engineers used the abacus as quickly and efficiently as our engineers use a slide rule. In the banks and business houses of antiquity the abacus was used just as our computing machines are today. The Romans had no trouble at all with their calculations, *provided* that they had the abacus handy. If an engineer forgot or lost his abacus he was surely in a bad way.

Thanks to the influence of the Arabs and Hindus, the abacus did not last long. With the introduction of their priceless system of nine digits and zero all arithmetical processes became so simple that children learned them in elementary school. To our nine numerals and zero we owe most of the comforts and luxuries that science and invention have given us. It is inconceivable how we could do without them. While they are commonly called Arabic, they are really Hindu-Arabic and they date back to the third century B.C., but they were not used in Europe until much later. It is also likely that the Egyptians and Persians played a part in developing the nine digits and zero system, and their trade from country to country gradually spread its use.

As Rome became more and more

involved in war and conquest, all thought of applying the inventions of Hero and others of the Hellenistic School to peacetime needs was set aside, and it remained for other scientists in other lands to carry on the torch. It was about this time in history that the Arabs and Chinese gave the world the first crude machines. They were the first to apply the gearwheels of Hero's useless inventions to the grinding of corn, the moving of heavy weights, and to scores of other useful purposes. They used the wind and the rapid flow of water as their source of power. These forces turned large wooden wheels, known to us as windmills and water wheels, which in turn moved other smaller wheels with cogs, which carried the power to still other, even smaller wheels that ground the flour. This was the first primitive machinery. In regions where water was scarce and the wind could not always be depended upon, animal power was used.

In addition to inventing the first crude machinery, the Arabs were great chemists. They were the first to describe and explain the processes of distillation, evaporation, filtration, and sublimation and to investigate the properties of acids, salts, and alkalis.

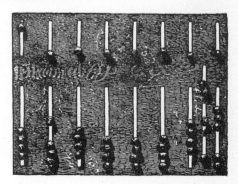

*The Roman abacus*

One of the greatest contributions to civilization was the invention of paper by a Chinese nobleman in the year 105 A.D. While experimenting with rags, mulberry bark, and hemp, Tsai Lun found that when wet and ladled on a screen the mixture lost its moisture and hardened into a sheet which was quite tough and durable. He rubbed this sheet with alum until it was smooth and furnished a fine writing surface. This was the first paper, made from rags and produced entirely by hand in separate sheets. Papermaking became a specialized art, invented by the Chinese and developed by the Arabs who established the first paper mill in Bagdad many centuries later. The Arabs were among the first people to make books by binding pages of paper together inside elaborate hand-tooled leather cases. The old Arabian books were masterpieces of art and craftsmanship.

The period of history from the fall of the Roman Empire in the fifth century A.D. to about the middle of the fifteenth century was not a fertile time for science and invention. With the decline of the ancient civilizations and the accompanying religious, political, and economic strife, European man needed many centuries to establish himself within a new framework of religious beliefs and moral values. In short, before he could once again take up the quest for information about the physical world, he required the security of a stable spiritual foundation.

But in the middle fourteen hundreds, the hunger for knowledge reasserted itself with such vigor that it seemed almost a rebirth of civilization. The Church began to encourage the bettering of man's earthly lot. Man's heavy burdens must be lifted from him and his life must be made easier. These preachings coming from such high authority helped to start a trend of thought toward machinery to do the heavy and arduous work of man. It was further encouraged by the intellectuals, who felt that the time was ripe for culture and creative thought to assert themselves after lying dormant for so many years. And so it was that men began once more to think for themselves and to devote part of that thinking to the creation of machines to make their lives easier. This was the very beginning of the Renaissance which flowered in Europe in the fifteenth and sixteenth centuries.

# CHAPTER III

# THE PROGRESS OF SCIENCE AND INVENTION IN THE MIDDLE AGES AND THE RENAISSANCE

When we think of machinery we naturally think of motion. A machine is a device which, by virtue of certain movements, accomplishes results which would otherwise require a great deal of time and human labor. When man first thought of using machinery, his main problem was to find a good, steady source of power to run it. Three sources were already well known: animal power, wind power, and water power. All of these had been used by the ancients but had never been thought of to any great extent in connection with machinery. Of the three, water power was found to be the most practical because it was the most dependable.

The water mill, which was used to grind corn many centuries before, began in the Middle Ages to take on other important tasks. It was made to turn a large circular iron saw and was thus able to save man days of hard labor sawing wood. In a short time it began to turn out lumber for building houses and making furniture. When made to operate a simple loom, it turned out fully ten times the amount of textiles formerly produced by hand. This, of course, was a great boon to the clothing makers of that time. But the most important use of the water mill was the one you would least suspect: the working of powerful bellows. Fires fanned by large bellows produced greater heat than had ever been attained before. With such heat, iron could be easily smelted from the ore and castings made.

Since iron could be cast into all kinds of forms and shapes, wheels and shafts were produced, and the science of mechanics was born. It was about this time that the crank, a means of translating rotary motion into reciprocal motion, was developed. A crank, in its simplest form, is a projection extending at right angles to a wheel, at the edge of the wheel, so that any long

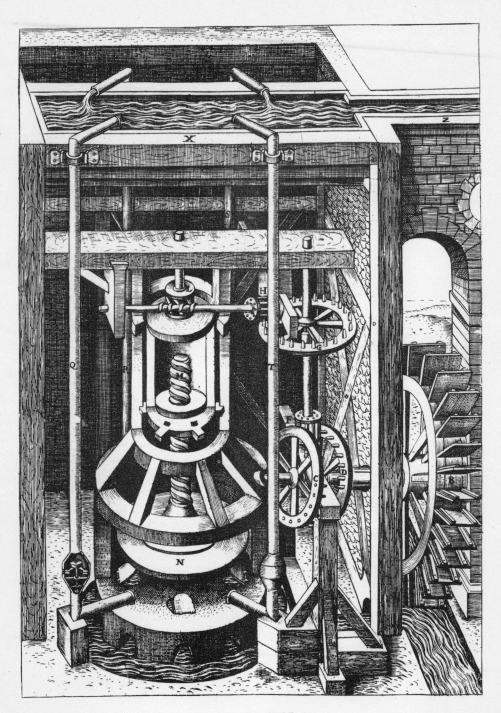

*A water mill of the Middle Ages*

arm attached to it will move back and forth as the wheel rotates (see the diagram). The crank and crankshaft is the basis of every engine and pump in the world today. The steam engine, the internal-combustion engine, and every other kind of engine, as well as every pump, are run by means of pistons and piston rods which are attached to cranks and crankshafts.

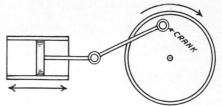

*A simple crank and how it transforms rotary motion into reciprocal motion— a most important invention*

Iron was used by the Greeks and Romans, but the invention of cast iron was undoubtedly the greatest technical achievement of the thirteenth century. Unfortunately, however, it was used mostly for purposes of destruction. Just about this time gunpowder and firearms were being manufactured on a large scale, and much effort was devoted to the casting of huge cannon. The many wars of the Middle Ages were raging and the country which had the most cannon had the best chance of victory. So, as important as the invention of cast iron was, it was not used for peaceful purposes until many years later.

Invention made enormous progress in the latter part of the period of history known as the Renaissance, which began in Italy in the fourteenth century and lasted for more than two hundred years. The word Renaissance, meaning *rebirth*, refers to the rebirth of culture and freedom of thought and expression after so many years of dormancy. It is the awakening again to the philosophy of the classical Greek and Roman periods and the desire to go forward and produce new and original works in art and science. One of the pioneers of the Renaissance was an Italian, Leonardo da Vinci, whom many historians consider the greatest genius of all times.

Leonardo enriched two different worlds: the world of art and the world of science and invention. The creator of such renowned masterpieces as the "Mona Lisa" and "The Last Supper" was also the creator of scores of mechanical inventions which were mostly responsible for starting the machine age. Inspired by Leonardo's mechanical genius, men like Ramelli, Besson, Zonca, and others wrote the first comprehensive books and treatises on mechanics and mechanical inventions. In these works as well as in Leonardo's famous notebooks, we find bevel gears, worm gears, conical screws, universal joints, ratchets, cams, various crank motions, link chains, belt drives, centrifugal pumps, and a great many other mechanical devices capable of producing hundreds of different motions. As Leonardo elaborated and improved upon the ancient inventions of Hero and took advantage of the five known fundamentals of all machines, so Ramelli and others improved on Leonardo and, by the beginning of the seventeenth century, the science of mechanics and mechanical engineering flourished.

Leonardo's notebooks show an

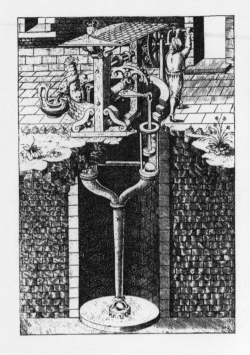

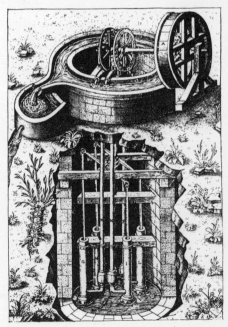

*Some of the 200 remarkable inventions of Ramelli*

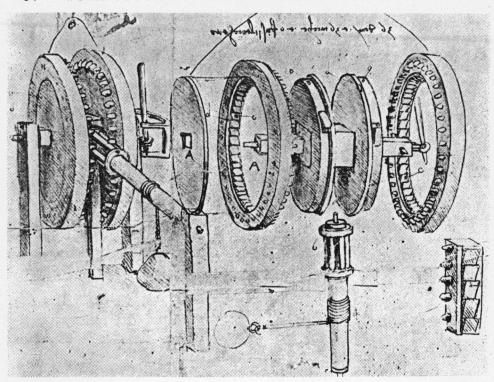

amazing variety of inventions. In addition to the various movements of gearwheels of many kinds, we find theories on wave motion (almost two centuries before Newton and Huygens), use of the pendulum (almost a century before Galileo), the hydraulic press, steam cannon, breach-loading cannon, machine-tool making, and many other vital devices for improving the crude machinery of that time. Ramelli's great work entitled *Le Diverse et Artificiose Machine,* published in 1588, was a remarkable compilation of the inventions and machinery of that day, and if you compare the illustrations taken from Ramelli with the illustrations taken from Leonardo's notes, you will see the similarity, particularly with respect to the way

in which the gears are made to work.

The impact of Leonardo and his followers was so great that, by the middle of the seventeenth century, thousands of young men were studying mechanics, and machine shops and tool designers began to appear in the large cities of Europe. All machine parts were made of wrought or cast iron. The process of making steel was not invented until 1856.

Science was progressing as it had never done before. Galileo, a young mathematician at the University of Padua, had already perfected a telescope through which he could see the moons of Jupiter. This same scientist formulated the fundamental concepts of matter and motion and the mathematical laws relating to them. Coper-

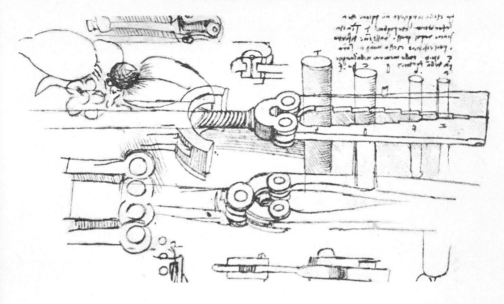

*Some of the wonderful inventions of Leonardo da Vinci*
*are shown here and on the facing page*

nicus had already "remade" astronomy by his discovery that the earth not only rotates on its axis but, with the other planets, revolves around the central sun. Francis Bacon and scores of other scientists added their original theories on the behavior of matter and the nature of the universe. They stressed the necessity of observation and experiment in order to penetrate into Nature's secrets. The only test of physical truth, they said, was actual experience directed by logic and mathematical reasoning. Faith alone was not enough for the scientists, and science and philosophy moved gradually away from their dependence on religion.

*But the greatest revolution in scientific thought was yet to come!* It started in 1655 when a shy and extremely delicate lad of twelve entered King's School at Grantham, England. Weak and unpopular boys usually attract bullies, so it was no wonder that a schoolboy fight started between the weakling and a bullying upperclassman. The weakling won the fight, and so did the world of modern science! So badly did Isaac Newton beat his opponent that the fellow had to suffer having his nose rubbed against the now famous wall.

Newton was not satisfied with his victory. For the first time in his life he had actually asserted himself and won out! He was going to beat this bully mentally as well as physically. He'd show him—and he did! His entire attitude changed, and a great genius for

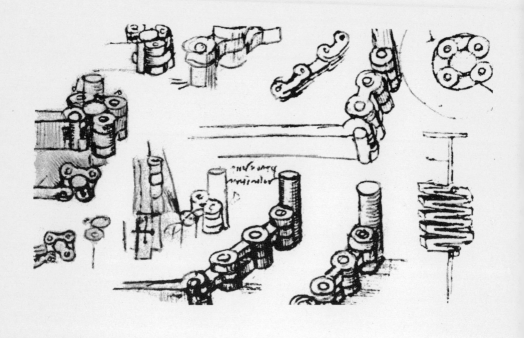

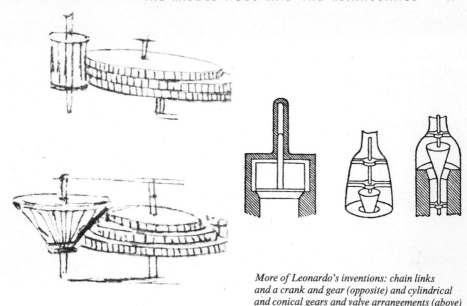

*More of Leonardo's inventions: chain links and a crank and gear (opposite) and cylindrical and conical gears and valve arrangements (above)*

science began to awaken within him. In a very short time he was the top-ranking student in King's School.

At Trinity College Newton's colossal brain sent him so far ahead of the other students that at the age of twenty-four he had produced *three of the greatest discoveries in the entire history of human thought!* These were the calculus, the nature and composition of light, and the law of universal gravitation.

Newton's life was long and fascinating, but his works are even more so. His famous *Principia,* or *Mathematical Principles of Natural Philosophy,* was published in three large volumes in 1686 and 1687. It has been called the greatest single contribution to science ever made by one man, the outstanding achievement of the human mind. The first two books, entitled "The Motion of Bodies," explain the laws and conditions of motion and force. The third book, "Of the System of the World," is a general summary of the gravitation law and most of the material in the two previous books. This Bible of Science is the starting point of every branch of modern engineering, astronomy, navigation, optics, and advanced mathematics.

With Newton's world-shaking discoveries and, more particularly, his conception and development of the calculus—the most powerful tool of science—the modern age was born. Though he was not an inventor, the far-reaching influence of his work laid the groundwork for the industrial revolution of the late eighteenth to the twentieth centuries, the epoch which produced nearly all of the world's greatest inventions.

# CHAPTER IV

# DEVELOPMENTS

# IN THE

# MECHANICAL AGE

## 1. The Story of Printing

More than five hundred years ago, in the town of Mainz, Germany, a son was born to Friele zum Gensfleisch and Elsgen Wyrich. His mother, Elsgen, who took the name of the town of her birth and was known as Elsgen zu Gutenberg, had the boy christened Johann Gutenberg.

Little is known of Johann's childhood, and certainly nobody knew that he was destined to be the inventor of movable type. As far as we know, he showed no special talent in any one particular field of endeavor. In 1438, at the age of thirty-nine, he formed a partnership with two other men and opened a little print shop in Strasbourg. In those days printing from type on presses was unknown. Printing was a highly specialized art, done from carefully carved wooden blocks on which the letters and designs were raised. The block was dipped in black dye and pressed by hand against cloth

or parchment. Prior to the time of Gutenberg there were no printed books. Books were written entirely by hand on parchment, and so rare and expensive that only wealthy noblemen could own them.

Although the idea of cutting each letter on a separate wooden block, a process that permitted adding many more individual letters and using them in various arrangements to suit one's needs, was ascribed to Gutenberg, a Dutchman by the name of Janszoon Coster of Haarlem was probably the originator. According to a well-known Chinese writer, movable type was invented by a Chinese artisan between 1041 and 1049, but little use was made of it, and the art was subsequently not highly developed. On this point historians differ, but it is generally agreed that Johann Gutenberg was the first man to take full advantage of the idea.

Movable type ranks in importance with the invention of the wheel, the taming of fire, the art of writing, and

*An artist's reproduction depicts Ottmar Mergenthaler demonstrating his machine to his first customer, Whitelaw Reid, editor of the* New York Tribune, *who is credited with naming it "the Linotype."*

*Ottmar Mergenthaler*

the discovery of electromagnetism. Without it there could be no spreading of knowledge except among the very few privileged people who could afford expensive handwritten books or books printed from wooden blocks.

The first book printed from movable metal type was the world-famous Gutenberg Bible published in 1454. Only 300 copies were printed, of which forty-five are in existence today.

The importance of movable type and the art of printing gradually spread throughout Europe, and, by the beginning of the sixteenth century, books appeared everywhere. This, of course, had a tremendous influence on culture. People began to read, and little by little the price of books tumbled until it was within the means of everyone. After a while, when the demand for news became acute, printers started to get out small sheets called newspapers. The first full-fledged newspaper to be known by name was the German *Frankfurter Zeitung* published in 1615.

As vital as movable type was in the printing of books, magazines, and newspapers, it had to be set by hand, and that took a lot of valuable time. Because of this, newspapers of any appreciable size were extremely rare. If you can imagine setting entirely by hand a newspaper like the Sunday edition of the New York *Times* with its almost 500 pages, you will soon appreciate the difficulty of the job.

Printers were aware of this great

# THE FIRST NEWSPAPER PAGE TO BE
## SET ON A LINOTYPE

The greater portion of this editorial page was composed on the first
commercial Linotype placed in a Newspaper Plant. It revolutionized com-
posing room methods and made possible the great Newspapers of today.

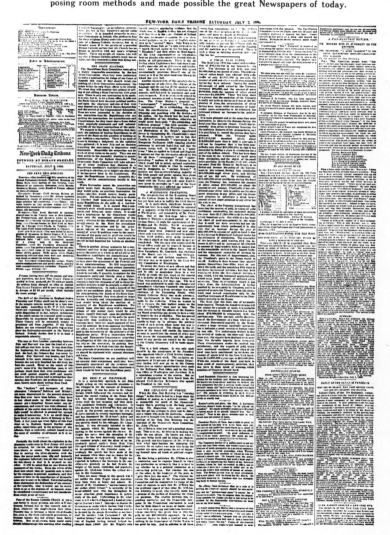

# N. Y. Tribune Editorial Page, July 3, 1886

*The first newspaper page set by Linotype
appeared on July 3, 1886, in the* New York Daily Tribune

*Improved in countless ways, modern Linotypes still depend on the basic principles of Ottmar Mergenthaler's machine*

drawback, but it wasn't until 1886 that something was done about it. In that year, Ottmar Mergenthaler invented and patented an extremely complicated machine which revolutionized printing, transforming it from a specialized art to a six-billion-dollar industry! His remarkable invention is known as the Linotype. It was first installed in the offices of the New York *Tribune* in the old Tribune Building on Park Row, New York. All the laborious, painstaking, and expensive features of hand-set type were eliminated. Pages of text could be set with as little effort as it takes to use a type-

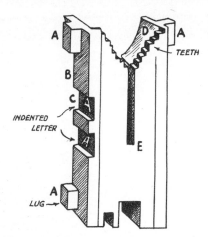

*A matrix with indented letters into which hot liquid type metal is poured*

writer, and in less than a tenth of the time it would require to set them by hand.

**THE LINOTYPE MACHINE.** The Linotype machine amazed everyone in the printing business, and in spite of its cost it was soon to be found everywhere printing was done. Today every daily newspaper, every book and magazine, and, in fact, practically all printed matter requiring more than a few pages of text, is set on the Linotype or Monotype machines.

The operator of a Linotype machine sits at a typewriterlike keyboard and punches out the copy he wants to set, just as though he were operating an ordinary typewriter. As each key is pressed, a small brass mold, called the matrix, with the appropriate letter cut into its edge, drops down the long incline onto a moving belt, which carries it to an assembly box and automatically places it next to the previous matrix. The spaces between the matrices and between the words are filled by wedges; some are narrow and some are wide, according to the nature of the measure, or width of the

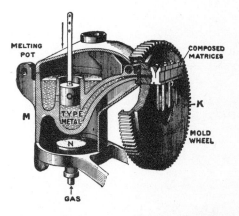

*Casting section, showing liquid type metal, plunger (O) forcing it into already composed matrices, and melting pot with gas jet (N)*

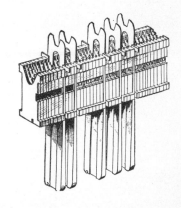

*Matrices lined up ready for filling with hot molten type metal*

line, in which the type is to be set. As soon as the line is completed and all the little matrices and space slugs are lined up on the side of the mold wheel, hot type metal, which has been melted by a gas flame under the melting pot, is forced by a plunger into the box containing the brass matrices and fills the incised letters in them. In less than a minute the liquid metal cools and hardens, and the entire line of type, in the form of one long slug, is ejected from the machine. A long lever comes down, picks up the matrices by the lugs (*A-A*) and places them on a long moving screw so they travel along to their respective slots and channels to drop down again and be reused. Each matrix has a different combination of notched teeth (*D*) in a triangular form and on the rod on which they slide there are different combinations of notched teeth also.

The operator doesn't have to wait for the previous slug to cool before starting the next. It is all done at the same time; while one slug is cooling, the matrices for the next slug are being lined up, so there is no delay. As each slug, or line of type, is ejected from the machine, it is placed on the printer's table directly under the previous slug, so that in a short time an entire page is assembled line by line. In the picture at the top of page 43, you will see the notches at the top of the matrix. Each letter has a different combination of notches, and as the letters slide along a grooved rod at the top of the machine, each drops into its respective slot and is ready for further duty.

As soon as the long galley pages are filled and all corrections made, they are arranged into the final page form of book, magazine, or newspaper, and the slugs are clamped together tightly and put into an electric bath where a copper electrotype is made of each page. Books are seldom printed from the original type; most of them are printed from electrotype plates made from this type. After each electrotype is made, the original type is melted down and used again in the Linotype machine to fill new matrices and the entire process is repeated.

**THE EARLY PRINTING PRESSES.** The printing press has come a long way since the days when Johann Gutenberg used his first movable type. The press of his day was a crude wooden

*An entire line of type appears on a slug, hence the name Linotype. Each slug is placed under the previous one until an entire page is ready for clamping and electroplating.*

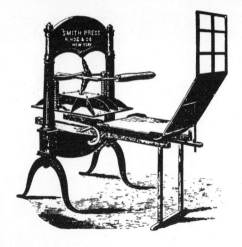

*Peter Smith hand press*

*Earliest form of printing press*

affair, consisting of two upright posts held together by heavy crosspieces, top and bottom. There were also two other big wooden crosspieces, one to hold the flat "bed" upon which the type was placed, and the other, a large wooden screw which was attached to a flat wooden "platen," screwed down and pressed on the type and paper in the same way that the old-fashioned office presses worked. The type was inked with a ball made of leather and stuffed with wool, and the ink was usually some concoction of dark dye. The operator spread paper over the inked type, laying a piece of blanket or some other soft material on it to keep the paper from tearing. The large screw was then turned by hand and the pressure of the paper on the type was gradually increased. This took a great deal of time, sometimes as much as three minutes per impression. Just imagine printing a full issue of a national magazine at the rate of three minutes a page: it would take about 5,000 years to produce a single edition!

This press continued in use for several hundred years. It wasn't until the end of the eighteenth century that printing presses were made entirely of cast iron and the old screw principle was discarded. George Clymer of Philadelphia was one of the first to do away with the screw and substitute long levers to get the necessary pressure. This improvement was made still more practical in 1827 by Samuel Rust, of New York, who added uprights at the sides, hollowed for the admission of iron bars that were very

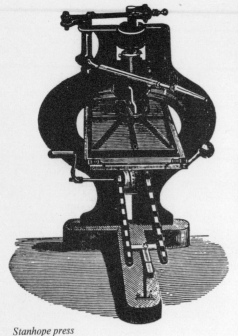

*Stanhope press*

securely riveted top and bottom. This gave a new look to the press, and Robert Hoe & Co. bought the patent and started making these new machines in 1828.

It took nearly 400 years for the printing press to evolve into what we might consider a fairly modern machine. The old screw hand press, after many years, gave way to the lever principle of making impressions, and while the lever principle was being explored and improved upon, many experiments were made on an entirely new and revolutionary design. Among the very first to make such experiments was a brilliant German engineer by the name of Friedrich Koenig, who visited England in 1806 and spent five years trying to harness power to a platen-type machine which he had invented.

It occurred to Koenig that a steam-motor-driven revolving cylin-

*Clymer's press*

der, pressing sheet after sheet against the flat type on a flat bed, could turn out printed pages much faster and better than the old vertical lever press. So in 1811 he got to work and made the first cylinder press. In this radically different printing press the form of type was placed on a flat bed with a cylinder directly above it. This cylinder had a threefold motion: the first third of the turn received the sheet upon one of the cylinders and secured it to it; the second third rolled along and took the impression of the type and permitted the sheet to be removed by hand; and the last third returned the tympan, empty, to receive another sheet. This was the first rotary press, the forerunner of the modern printing press. Two years after he made this new machine, Koenig patented an important improvement. The part of the periphery of the cylinder not used for taking the impression of the type was slightly reduced in diameter, so as to allow the form to return under it freely after the impression. This new press also carried a movable type bed geared to the sides of the machine and free to slide back and forth in a reciprocating motion.

Friedrich Koenig's invention was as important to printing as Mergenthaler's Linotype was to typesetting. All high-speed presses throughout the world today are rotary presses. Nearly every newspaper, magazine, and book is printed on highly improved cylinder rotary presses, based on the principle discovered and patented by Koenig.

Koenig's first press printed the London *Times* and turned it out at the rate of 1,100 per hour. Many improvements for printing and handling the sheets were subsequently made, and double-cylinder presses were able to print 4,000 sheets per hour.

*An early Hoe and Adam's platen press*

*Largest model of the Hoe Eighteen Unit Streamline Super-Production Color-Convertible press*

In 1845 the American firm of R. Hoe & Co., which had been making all kinds of printing presses for years, brought out a further improvement on the Koenig press. It was called the Hoe Type Revolving Machine, and was capable of turning out 8,000 printed newspapers per hour. It printed the Philadelphia *Ledger* in 1846.

As the demand for newspapers, magazines, and books became greater and greater, the improvements on high-speed rotary presses increased. In 1871 R. Hoe & Co. installed the first very extra-high-speed press in the printing rooms of the New York *Tribune*. This press had a speed of 18,000 papers an hour. A short time later, Hoe produced the Octuple press

turning out hundreds of printed and folded newspapers a minute. Composed of more than a thousand parts and weighing sixty tons, this press was the forerunner of all our high-speed presses of today.

**THE MODERN PRINTING PRESSES.** Few inventions in history have been worked over and improved as much as the printing press. Today there are all kinds of presses. There are printing presses for turning out circulars and booklets in huge quantities. There are large presses for turning out books such as this one. There are enormous printing presses, some of them three stories high, capable of turning out newspapers at the astounding rate of 360,000 per hour: an entire newspaper like the New York *Daily News* or *Mir-*

*ror* printed, cut, folded, and stacked at the rate of 360,000 per hour or 6,000 a minute.

The majority of all newspaper presses today are rotary presses, but, instead of the paper being held on the drum and the type matter placed on a flat deck as is the case with most other printing presses, the type matter is curved and placed around the cylinder. This is done by means of electrotyped forms—copper electrotypes of the original newspaper page curved in a quarter circle, four of them to one cylinder, or drum.

The machine built by R. Hoe & Co. known as the Hoe Eighteen Unit Streamline Super-Production Color-Convertible press is the very latest in the advanced art of printing-press design. Here are just a few details of this amazing machine: It is composed of eighteen distinct printing sections, or units, and three streamline "super-production" double folders. Each unit is composed of two plate cylinders and two impression cylinders. The former carry the curved electrotype plates from which the actual printing is done, and the latter press the paper against these plates. The printing units are equipped with a patented pump system of ink distribution, the greatest improvement in newspaper press construction since the invention of the triangular former folder of seventy years ago. The pump system of ink distribution consists of thirty-two small pumps that work in unison and assure even, accurate distribution of ink. The unprinted white paper, in rolls five feet wide and forty inches in

*Kelly press with lock-up and swing-back delivery*

diameter, is placed on reels below the press and run through the units, passing between the plate and the impression cylinders, where it is printed first on one side and then on the other. From there it is led over rollers to the streamline double folder, slit, and led from the V-shaped "formers," through nipping rollers to the folding cylinder, where the sheets are cut to the proper length by a special form of knife on the cutting cylinders. At the same time, the papers receive their fold and are then delivered on an endless belt, completely finished in every way and ready for distribution.

Some idea of the enormous speed and accuracy of this press can be obtained from the fact that within an hour over fifty-four tons of paper, totaling approximately 370 miles in length, go through these three presses

and folders and are turned into finished newspapers.

The familiar Kelly press used in most large printing establishments is shown in the illustrations. It takes a sheet 17½" x 22" and has a speed range of between 2,800 and 4,200 printed sheets per hour. The picture on page 49 shows the paper piled up and open from the rear of the machine. Here you can see the type matter lying on the flat bed. These forms can be locked right onto the bed of the press. The paper stock is lifted automatically and fed into the running press. When the paper gets close to the suction holes, it is picked up and brought in contact with a number of very rapidly moving wheels, and from these wheels it is led into the large cylinder drum, which turns at high speed and presses the blank sheet

*The Kelly ready for action*

against the flat type bed, which is inked by the numerous rollers seen in the illustration. After going through the press, it is led out the rear end and stacked up in printed form.

This, briefly, is what presses are like today. Some of them print four colors at once and perform what the early inventors would call miracles.

## 2. The Story of Optics

**THE FIRST LENS.** Hundreds of millions of lives have been saved by curved glass. Hundreds of millions of eyes have been helped toward better vision, and countless millions of people have been entertained by curved glass through books, magazines, newspapers, the movies, and television. Without this curved glass, otherwise known as the lens, there could be no microscope, and the sciences of optics and bacteriology, which have wiped out the epidemics and plagues of years ago, would be unknown. Photography would also be unknown, and millions of us would be cheated out of proper vision. Navigation would be in a bad way without the lens; so would surveying and mapping and modern building, since all engineers' transits contain telescopes.

As vital and important as the lens is, nobody knows who actually invented it. The magnifying power of glass balls was known to the ancients, and very crude lenses made of rock crystal have been found among the ruins of Nineveh. These lenses were far too crude to be of any use. An Italian named Salvino D'Armato, of the Armati of Florence, is credited with being the inventor of curved-

*Ink distribution
in the modern Kelly press*

glass spectacles in 1285, and, according to another reliable source, Nicholas Bullet, a French priest, first used curved-glass spectacles in 1282 to help him read and sign important documents. Either or both of these men may have been the inventor of eyeglasses, for it is reasonably sure that before 1280 such an invention was quite unknown.

The idea of glasses placed in frames and worn in front of the eyes to improve vision grew as more and more people were helped by them. In 1483 the Guild of Master Spectacle Makers was formed in Nuremberg, and opticians began to practice their profession all over Europe.

But here again history is not too informative. Just how the microscope and telescope grew from a knowledge of the spectacle lens is not too clear. Apparently spectacles were worn for nearly a hundred years before the microscope and telescope were born. In 1608 Hans Lippershey, a spectacle maker in Wesel, Germany, was testing the power of two spectacle lenses by holding them up to some distant object and moving them in a rotary motion, just the way opticians do today. By chance one of the spectacle lenses got in front of the other and they were focused together on a distant steeple of a church. To Lippershey's amazement, the steeple appeared much nearer than it ordinarily did, and this started a long series of experiments which resulted in the invention of the first telescope.

Lippershey's telescope was indeed crude; just two lenses in a tube, one behind the other, but it *did* work to a certain extent. It remained for Galileo Galilei to improve on it and produce the first practical telescope. In 1609 he demonstrated his instrument from the tower of St. Mark's in Venice. He turned it toward a distant building a few miles away and was able to see the detail work clearly. He then turned it on nearer objects and found that he could examine them just as though they were three feet away. Some time later he brought a number of the leading citizens to witness his invention, and it was then that he turned a more powerful telescope toward the sky and saw for the first time a number of moons close to the planet Jupiter and a distinct ring around the planet Saturn. So startling was this discovery that Galileo became world-famous and was credited with being the inventor of the telescope.

The microscope was invented somewhere around the beginning of the seventeenth century, but who actually invented it nobody knows. Robert Hooke and Nehemiah Grew are given credit, but there were many others in the field, all experimenting at about the same time. Marcello Malpighi, a brilliant Italian physiologist, was the first to apply the microscope to the study of animal and vegetable structure, and is considered the founder and father of microscopic anatomy. He was the first man to see blood coursing through the tiny tubes in the network of the lungs and the first to describe and demonstrate respiration in the human body.

The microscope began to take its place beside the world's greatest inventions with the astonishing and far-reaching discoveries of Anton van Leeuwenhoek, a Dutch scientist who was the father of the science of bacteriology. Leeuwenhoek discovered tiny microorganisms in rain water, and in a number of drawings given to the Royal Society in Amsterdam in 1683 he pictured bacteria for the first time. He sent 110 papers to that society and twenty-seven papers to the French Academy, reporting hundreds of different microscopical observations, which were so important that they revised the scientific thought of that period and those that followed.

Leeuwenhoek made his own microscopes, 247 of them altogether, all remarkable instruments in spite of their simplicity. At his death in 1723 it was revealed that he had designed 419 lenses, most of which were the double convex type, which is the kind used in photography and moving-picture projection today. This modest, patient man was responsible for the saving of millions and millions of lives and the prevention and elimination of plagues and epidemics. It is more than likely that we owe the first practical lens to him. But, while the value of the lens was known at that time, its vast applications had to wait for the development of the science of optics by pioneers like Huygens.

At an early age Christian Huygens showed unusual aptitude for mathematics and science, and at twenty-six he invented the pendulum clock, as well as a new method of grinding and polishing lenses, the principle of which is used to this day. Most of his later life was devoted to optics. In 1681 he started making lenses with very long focal lengths—that is, long distances from the image to the lens— a thing unheard of in those days. After six years of research he produced the first large telescopes with eyepieces having focal lengths of 180 and 210 feet.

Newton was the first to show that light is composed of many different colors and that when light is bent these colors appear in the form of a spectrum. He explained this in terms of waves, wave lengths, and vibrations.

The thoughts and researches of these men enabled the scientists that followed to formulate new laws of op-

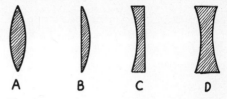

*This shows the four types of lenses. A is double convex. B is plano-convex. C is plano-concave. D is double concave.*

tics based on the nature of light rays, and soon photographic lenses began to appear. Instead of one piece of double convex glass, these lenses consisted of several pieces cemented together in many different ways.

**MODERN OPTICS.** While the subject of optics is a difficult one involving many mathematical formulas and requiring a knowledge of mathematics, the fundamentals of the simple lens can be understood by anyone. We know from observation that, when light travels from a rare to a denser medium, it is slightly bent. It doesn't travel quite as fast in water or glass as it does in air. This bending is called refraction.

The principal lenses that we shall consider here are shown in diagram above. The double convex lens is the one most frequently used, since it is a magnifying lens as well as a projecting lens. Both the surfaces of a double

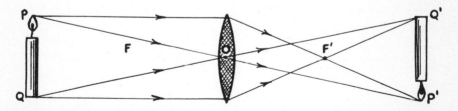

*Double convex lens with the two foci F and F' and optical center O.*
*Rays from candle PQ are bent when passing through lens and pass through F'. All unbent rays pass through O. Where these meet the image will be formed upside down Q'P'.*

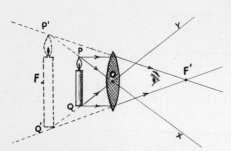

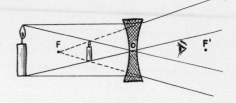

This double concave lens is a reducing glass. The eye is between the focus F′ and the lens and you can see how the image is reduced.

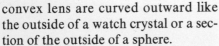

*This shows the double convex lens when the eye is between the focus F′ and the lens. Rays from candle PQ pass through F′ as before, but are projected back to meet rays that pass through O, projected back. The result is an enlarged image P′Q′. This is a magnifying glass.*

convex lens are curved outward like the outside of a watch crystal or a section of the outside of a sphere.

Through the center of the lens a line may be drawn perpendicular to the lens itself. This is called the principal axis and the point $O$ in the very center of the lens is called the optical center. All rays that pass through this optical center pass undisturbed and are not bent or refracted. It is the only point in the lens where there is no bending of rays. All other rays that pass through the lens are bent or refracted in different degrees according to their distance from $O$. It must be remembered that rays going through a lens always bend toward the thicker portion of the lens. Another important thing to remember is that all bent or refracted rays pass through a point outside the lens which is called the principal focus. The distance from the principal focus to the lens is called the focal length, and that is what the $f$ stands for in the camera. When we say the camera lens is set for $f$ 8, we mean

that the distance from the principal focus to the lens is eight times the diameter of the lens.

Remembering that all rays from an object pass through the optical center as well as the principal focus, you can easily see, by means of the diagram on page 53, how images are formed. We see first a double convex lens with its two principal foci, $F$ and $F'$. Let a candle $PQ$ be placed behind one of these foci, as shown. A ray of light from $P$ passes through $O$ and is not refracted. All other parallel rays are refracted and pass through the principal focus $F'$; where they meet the ray which has passed through the optical center $O,$ the image is formed. You can see from the diagram why the image is upside down.

Suppose now that the candle is placed between the focus $F$ and the lens and viewed from the other side. A ray from $P$ passes unrefracted through the optical center $O$ and is projected back along the line $OX$. The same holds true for a ray from $Q$ that passes unrefracted along the line $OY$. At the same time, all parallel rays from $P$ and $Q$ are refracted and pass through $F'$, and are projected back to meet $PX$ and $QY$ where a much larger

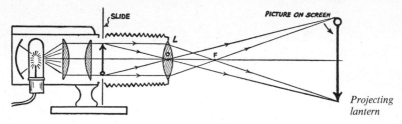

*Projecting lantern*

image is formed, this time right side up. This is a clear diagrammatic explanation of why a magnifying glass, which is a double convex lens, enlarges objects.

Just as double convex lens enlarges, so a double *concave* lens reduces. This is otherwise known as a reducing glass and is used occasionally, together with other lenses, in the construction of optical instruments.

The projecting lantern is extremely important to all of us, for there would be no movies without it. In principle it is the reverse of a camera. In the camera the object is at a distance from the lens and the image is nearby; in the projecting lantern the object (film or slide) is near the lens and the image is far away on a large screen. The slide is placed in the lantern as shown, and a powerful light is sent through it. This light first passes through two plano-convex lenses, and after passing through the slide or film, it is sent through the double convex lens *L,* which enlarges and projects the picture (upside down) on a distant screen. The lens *L* can be adjusted for various distances from the screen and, of course, all slides are put in the lantern upside down so that they are projected right side up.

The microscope consists essentially of a double convex lens known as the objective (*O*), which is placed close to the tiny object to be magnified. A strong light is now sent through the object by means of the mirror, and an enlarged image of the object is formed at *P* just at the right distance from the powerful magnifying lens *L'* to cause a tremendous magnification of an already greatly magnified object. The resulting image, shown by the heavy arrow, has a magnification of between 1,000 and 2,000 diameters. Most light microscopes view the objects by transmitted light, that is, light shining *through* an object placed on a glass slide.

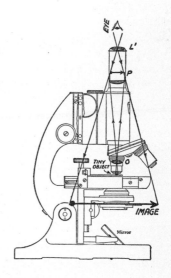

*Microscope*

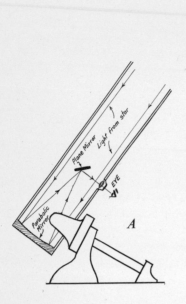

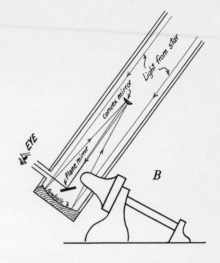

The two types of reflector telescopes.
A is the Newtonian; B the Cassegrain.

**THE WORLD'S LARGEST EYE.** Any person living in a big city has probably seen the sidewalk astronomer with his large telescope pointed at the moon or at some planet. It is usually ten cents a look, and you do not see very much for your money. The telescope he uses is of the refractor type, in which a double convex lens when focused on a distant object produces an image in the space inside the telescope tube. This image is enlarged by one or more lenses in the eyepiece, and a great magnification results. The lens of the refractor telescope is seldom more than thirty-six inches in diameter, although the one at the Yerkes Observatory is forty inches. The uses for such a telescope are limited, because when light passes through a lens a small percentage of it is lost or absorbed by the glass, and if the telescope contains a number of lenses, a considerable amount of the light will be absorbed.

For astronomical work the reflector telescope is nearly always used. This consists primarily of a large concave mirror placed at one end of a long tube. The rays of light entering from the star, of course, are parallel to each other. This is because the star is so many billions of miles away that the point from which the rays emanate (the star) may be considered as an infinite distance. When these parallel rays strike the reflecting mirror they are brought to a focus—a point somewhere up the tube of the telescope. It is here that they are examined and analyzed. They are usually photographed or sent through a prism for analysis of their spectra to determine the composition of the star in question and the elements present.

There are two main types of reflector telescopes: the Newtonian and the Cassegrain. You can see from the diagrams that it is just a question of where the eyepiece is which determines the differences in these telescopes. In the Newtonian telescope a plane mirror reflects the focused beam at right angles to the telescope tube, as shown. In the Cassegrain telescope the beam is reflected in several ways, sometimes right back through a hole in the center of the reflecting mirror and sometimes through a plane mirror at the bottom of the telescope, as shown.

The advantage of the reflector telescope over the refractor type is mainly that of greater light intensity. There is practically no loss of light in reflector telescopes because the rays of light do not have to pass through glass.

We come now to an interesting fact which very few people realize in connection with telescopes. We all think that the major function of a large reflector telescope in any one of our observatories is to magnify the distant stars and planets. When the great mirror was cast for the giant 200-inch Palomar telescope it aroused unusual public interest. This wonderful achievement in the casting of glass required the highest type of skill and knowledge on the part of the makers at the Corning Glass Works in Corning, N. Y. It took eleven months for this gigantic 4½-inch slab to cool because the slightest quickening of the cooling process might have caused unevenness and strain, thus rendering the mirror useless. The cooling had to be mechanically regulated to the fraction of a degree. And the glass had to be watched day and night. When it was finally ready for shipment many people exclaimed: "Now, at last, we shall be able to see the moon as though it were only twenty-five miles away!" or "Now we shall be able to know whether there is life on Mars!" This is a natural assumption but it is not a scientific one.

One of the chief purposes of this colossal eye is to gather as much light as can be gathered and analyze it through the spectroscope in order to solve some of the riddles of distant suns. One of the main difficulties in the past was that the light from distant stars or suns was too weak to give a clear spectrum, and thus the analysis of the spectrum became particularly difficult. By intensifying the light from the distant stars we can learn a great deal more about their nature.

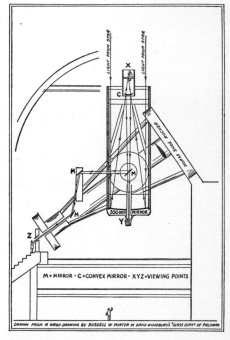

*Diagrammatic picture of the great Hale telescope at Mt. Palomar*

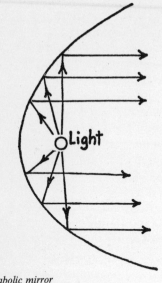

*Parabolic mirror*
*reflecting parallel light rays*

Another important use for this new marvel is for the penetration of outer space. Twice as large as any other telescope in existence, it will be capable of concentrating 800,000 times as much light as is captured by the human eye. This means that it is 800,000 times more powerful than our sight. Whereas we are capable at best of seeing only from 3,000 to 4,000 stars on a clear night, this great eye enables us to discern 3,000,000,000 of them.

As you know, the Milky Way looks like a cloud to the naked eye. Through the 100-inch reflector telescope at Mt. Wilson Observatory we see that it is composed of millions and millions of suns, most of them much bigger than our sun. Through the new 200-inch telescope we shall be able to peer further into outer space and see billions of these suns and to penetrate the universe to a distance exceeding 2,000,000,000 light years!

On the whole, the appearance, preparation, and complex manipulation of the world's largest telescope is disappointing to most of us who had visualized a glorified sidewalk telescope for spying on the moon and planets. It may seem peculiar that astronomers are reluctant to use this huge eye for viewing comparatively nearby heavenly bodies. But it is not designed for that purpose and, as a matter of fact, would be cumbersome and clumsy even though it could do the job fairly well. To quote from one astronomer: "It would be like using the 'Queen Mary' to cross a river instead of using a ferryboat."

The reflecting mirror is not a section of a huge sphere, as one might imagine. It is a section of a paraboloid, shaped somewhat like the reflecting mirrors in automobile and locomotive headlights. The parabolic mirror has the important property of sending out all rays of light parallel from a given point, as shown in the diagram. Of course the reverse is also true, and that is why this mirror is so important in the telescope. All rays from a given star come into the telescope parallel to one another. As soon as they strike the mirror they are brought to a focus, and it is mostly at this focus that the given star is observed. The larger the parabolic mirror, the greater the light-gathering properties, so the enormous 200-inch mirror can concentrate the light of a given star on a point and magnify it many hundreds of times. This means that a good spectrum analysis can be made from its light, and the composition of the star can be determined as well as its distance and size.

Christopher L. Sholes, the inventor
of the typewriter

## 3.  The Story of the Typewriter

If you happened to be living in Milwaukee in the winter of 1866 and dropped in on Mr. Kleinsteuber's machine shop at noon on a certain day in January, you would have seen a little group of men huddled around a workbench, vehemently arguing the merits of a machine for numbering the pages of blank books. And you would have listened to the inventor, Christopher Latham Sholes, a middle-aged man and a printer by trade, discussing the finishing touches on the newly made model with his co-inventors, Samuel Soule and Carlos Glidden, while Kleinsteuber and Schwalbach, the patternmaker, looked on.

If you had been there, you undoubtedly would not have realized that a turning point in modern civilization was marked right in that little machine shop when Glidden turned to

Sholes and said, "Sholes, why can't you make a machine that will print letters instead of numbers? If you can make a successful numbering machine, I should think you could make a successful writing machine."

For six months Sholes thought about Glidden's suggestion—a writing machine and how it might be invented—but he did nothing about it. The trigger that finally set him off was an article which appeared in the *Scientific American* for July 1867. Written by Alfred Beach, it foretold the enormous possibilities a writing machine had and what it could do for the legal profession alone. "A practical writing machine," the article said, "means a revolution almost as great as that caused by the invention of

The birthplace of the typewriter:
Kleinsteuber's shop in Milwaukee

*French typewriter, 1833*

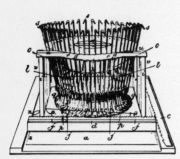

*Thurber's typewriter*

*Beach typewriter*

printing in the world of books." Inspired by this, Sholes got to work in earnest.

The idea of a writing machine was not new at that time. As early as 1714 Queen Anne had granted a patent to Henry Mill, an engineer in London, for "an artificial machine or method of impressing or transcribing letters," but all records of that machine were lost and there was no model made of it. A complicated and quite impractical writing machine was invented by M. Pogin of Marseilles, France, in 1833, and Charles Thurber of Worcester, Massachusetts, took out a patent on his "printing machine" in August, 1843, twenty-three years before Sholes started his work. These machines were more ingenious than practical, and they failed to stand up against the wear and tear of the necessary pounding. It was up to Sholes and his untiring and persistent efforts, as well as those of his co-inventors and backers, to produce the first practical typewriter.

It took Sholes and his colleagues seven discouraging years to find the answers to all the problems. The first thing he did was to go to his friend Charlie Weller, a telegraph operator, and show him his odd-looking machine, consisting of a telegraph key which, when pressed down, sent a little metal type letter smack against a glass plate. With the aid of carbon paper (a rare thing in those days) it would "print" the letter on paper placed on the glass. But this crude device could print only one letter, and a practical typewriter must have forty or more characters. The key idea was good, but the rest of the machine had

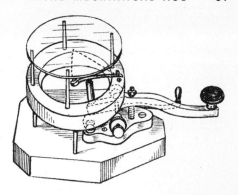

*Sholes' first typewriter key*

to be discarded as being impractical.

Charlie Weller proved to be a great help and inspiration to Sholes and his two partners. He was well acquainted with court records and knew the drudgery of handwritten reports. He volunteered to test and get constructive criticism and suggestions on the first machines that came out of the Kleinsteuber shop, to see if they could stand the gaff of court reporting and the incessant pounding necessary for court records.

The first machine produced by Sholes in 1867 was still a crude affair with a keyboard somewhat like that of a piano. Only capital letters were used, but it did have a roller and a movable carriage, and it even had a lever for turning the paper from line to line. Though wobbly and inaccurate, the machine actually did work, and Sholes wrote numerous letters on it, mailing them out to his friends and business acquaintances as curiosities. One of these letters, addressed to a Mr. James Densmore of Meadville, Pennsylvania, made such an impression that he wrote Sholes, asking what he would want for a partnership. The three partners quickly answered Densmore, saying that a quarter interest was his if he would pay all past expenses. Densmore was so excited with the idea of a writing machine that, in spite of his being a shrewd and crafty businessman, he promptly accepted without inquiring how much the past expenses were or requesting to see the machine.

When Densmore finally did see the machines Sholes and his partners were turning out, he was disgusted and declared them to be junk, good only to demonstrate that the idea was feasible.

And then began the real headaches and heartaches. Machine after machine was made under the critical eye of Densmore, but each in turn broke down only a few weeks after its initial test. In the following years, more than fifty typewriters were built at a cost of

*Early model of Sholes' typewriter*

$250 each, and the Densmore money dwindled rapidly. Each time he put up more money, he demanded more interest in the invention, until he almost went broke but owned nearly all the stock.

Fortunately, at this point a Mr. Yost entered the picture, and it was a lucky thing for the business world that he did. Yost was an experienced engineer who knew the value of extreme accuracy in machinery. He was amazed when he saw the kind of machines Sholes and his associates were building. To him they were hopelessly sloppy, made by men who lacked experience in precision machinery. But while he found fault with Sholes' typewriters, he also realized the great value of such machines, provided they could be made by highly skilled mechanics.

At that time some of the most accurate precision work was done by mechanics employed in the manufacture of guns and firearms. If guns were not true to a thousandth of an inch, they had to be scrapped. Precision and accuracy were absolutely essential in gun manufacture. So it was logical for Yost to approach one of America's leading gunsmiths and manufacturers of firearms, E. Remington & Sons Co., at Ilion, New York.

The Remingtons saw at once the enormous possibilities of the typewriter, and in 1873 they bought out Sholes and his partners, retaining their own name. The first typewriter sold to the public bore the name "Remington."

The Remington Company put their skilled mechanics to work to perfect

*Sholes' typewriter showing treadle*

the machine, and very gradually it began to take the form of the modern typewriter with its shift key giving upper- and lower-case letters and its self-winding ribbon and carriage. The original arrangement of the letters was kept (although nobody knows just why the keys were arranged that way in the first place), and typewriters began to appear in the shops.

Only 400 typewriters were sold in 1874, the first year, and many of them were returned because of defects. The public did not respond readily to this newfangled writing machine, and the first efforts to sell them were quite discouraging. It took many years of research and experimenting to produce successful typewriters, and it looked as though it would take many more years to educate the public to use them.

BJUYT KIOP M LKJHGFDSA!QWERTYUIOP:_-0876543297 R⁻
HA

                              HARTFORD, DEC. 9,
DEAR BROTHER:
I AM TRYING T TO GET THE HANG OF THIS NEW F
FANGLED WRITING MACHINE, BUT AM NOT MAKING
A SHINING SUCCESS OF IT.  HOWEVER THIS IS THE
FIRST ATTEMPT I EVER HAVE MADE, & YET I PER-
CEIVETHAT I SHALL SOON & EASILY ACQUIRE A FINE
FACILITY IN ITS USE.  I SAW THE THING IN BOS-
TON THE OTHER DAY & WAS GREATLY TAKEN WITH
IT.  SUSIE HAS STRUCK THE KEYS ONCE OR TWICE,
& NO DOUBT HAS PRINTED SOME LETTERS WHICH DO
NOT BELONG WHERE SHE PUT THEM.
THE HAVING BEEN A COMPOSITOR IS LIKELY TO BE
A GREAT HELP TO ME, SINCE O NE CHIEFLY NEEDS
SWIFTNESS IN BANGING THE KEYS. THE MACHINE COSTS
125 DOLLARS. THE MACHINE HAS SEVERAL VIRTUES
I BELIEVE IT WILL PRINT FASTER THAN I CAN WRITE.
ONE MAY LEAN BACK IN HIS CHAIR & WORK IT.  IT
PILES AN AWFUL STACK OF WORDS ON ONE PAGE.
IT DONT MUSS THINGS OR SCATTER INK BLOTS AROUND.
OF COURSE IT SAVES PAPER.

                              SUSIE IS GONE,
NOW, & I FANCY I SHALL MAKE BETTER PROGRESS.
WORKING THIS TYPE-WRITER REMINDS ME OF OLD
ROBERT BUCHANAN, WHO, YOU REMEMBER, USED TO
SET UP ARTICLES AT THE CASE WITHOUT PREVIOUS-
LY PUTTING THEM IN THE FORM OF MANUSCRIPT. I
WAS LOST IN ADMIRATION OF SUCH MARVELOUS
INTELLECTUAL  CAPACITY.
                              LOVE TO MOLLIE.
                         YOUR BROTHER,
                              SAM.

*Mark Twain's first typewritten letter, December 9, 1874 (Copyright by Harper & Bros.)*

*First Remington typewriter*

*Modern typewriter*

As far as is known, the first purchaser of a typewriter was Mark Twain, who saw it displayed in a Boston shop. His letter shows what he thought of it.

As time went on and the typewriter became more and more practical, lawyers, authors, and businessmen everywhere began to wake up to its convenience, to say nothing of the enormous time it saved. Girls were taught to use it, and gradually thousands of jobs were thrown open to women who had never before had an opportunity to become financially independent.

In 1882 Wyckoff, Seamans & Benedict obtained control of the machine, and in fourteen years 200,000 were made and sold. The more the word spread about the wonders of the typewriter, the more the public clamored for it. Businessmen wanted bookkeeping machines as well as typewriters; authors cried for a small, light, portable typewriter. Edison and other inventors got busy working out such machines. John T. Underwood started manufacturing improved typewriters in 1895, and thus the modern portable typewriter was born.

Today the typewriter is a *must* in every business house in the civilized world, from tiny "holes in the wall" to corporations the size of General Motors. The little machine that Sholes and his associates planned in Kleinsteuber's machine shop, back in the winter of 1866, has now become one of the world's most important inventions.

### 4. The Story of the Sewing Machine

Very often a great inventor, either because of extreme modesty or total lack of business ability, dies unknown and unheralded, while his inventions live on to simplify and ease the lives of millions. Such is the case of Walter Hunt, a brilliant student and creative genius who for twenty-five years bristled with practical and important inventions, but never did anything to exploit them.

Among Hunt's repertoire of inventions, we find all kinds of improvements on firearms, ice plows, paraffin candles, velocipedes, and machinery for making nails and rivets. He'd get a marvelous idea, make a model of it, use it for whatever purpose it was intended, forget it, and go on to the next

*Walter Hunt, who invented the sewing machine before Howe*

invention. Seldom did he patent any-thing, and he never thought of making money from any of his ideas. That was the way with Walter Hunt, and nobody could change him.

Somewhere between the years 1832 and 1834 in a little shop on Amos Street, New York City, Hunt con-ceived and made the first sewing ma-chine. It contained most of the essential parts of our modern sewing machine. Hunt used the eye-pointed needle, which was moved by a vibrat-ing arm and worked with a shuttle carrying a second thread, so as to make an interlocked stitch. Like everything else, this machine was put aside for other ideas, and when Hunt applied for a patent in 1853, it was refused him on the grounds of aban-donment. The Hunt machine was found many years later in the attic of his house, long after another man had become famous as the inventor of the sewing machine.

It all started in Boston in 1839 over a heated argument between the owner of a little machine shop and a fellow mechanic. The argument ended with: "Well, go ahead and do it, and I'll as-sure you an independent fortune." The "do it" referred to the making of a practical machine that would sew, and the two men little realized the enormous impact of their words on the shy, curly-haired farm boy em-ployed in that shop.

Young Elias, because of his inef-ficiency and lameness, hated his work. It was drudgery and often painful. The two or three dollars a week that he earned for working six ten-hour days vanished in the sudden day-dream of "do it" and "I'll assure you

*Elias Howe*

an independent fortune." Young and inexperienced as he was, he made up his mind then and there to "do it," and no amount of adversity or dis-couragement could ever keep him from his goal. And he did it!

Elias left the machine shop for a slightly better job as machinist at $9.00 per week. On this salary he mar-ried, and before long had three babies to feed and clothe. Not being able to better himself financially, he spent all of his spare time watching his wife while she sewed for herself and the babies. How could he ever make a machine that would go through those complicated motions?

It seemed impossible and hopeless to copy the motions of a human hand; most other men in Howe's predica-ment would have given up and never thought about it again. But Elias Howe was no ordinary man. He had

*Original sewing machines made by Howe in 1845*

an amazing flair for mechanics, especially when he could be his own boss, and his aim was an independent fortune. He thought and thought and thought, and early in the spring of 1844 he hit upon the idea of using two threads and making stitches with the aid of a shuttle. This was the first encouragement he had had, and in October of that year, out of savings he had scraped together, he made the first model of a crude sewing machine. Unable to perfect it because of lack of funds, he moved his family to his father's house in Cambridge, Massachusetts, and started looking for work there. It was hopeless at that time to continue experimenting, since he was penniless and had to depend upon his father for support.

More determined than ever to make a sewing machine as soon as he found work, he had the good luck to meet George Fisher, a former schoolmate. Fisher instantly saw in his friend the makings of genius, and the idea of a sewing machine appealed to him. He offered Howe free board for him and his family, and agreed to advance $500 for tools and supplies to make a workable model. In return for this he asked for a 50 per cent interest in the invention. Of course, Howe was overjoyed with this proposition, and in December 1844 the Howe family moved into the home of George Fisher.

With a certain peace of mind in knowing that his wife and children would be taken care of while he worked feverishly day and night on his new idea, Howe produced a machine that actually sewed two suits of clothes. While this odd-looking device was not really the world's first sewing machine, it *was* the great-grandfather of our present machines. It may be seen today in the U. S. National Museum in Washington, D. C. Howe patented it in 1845 and started out to convince the world what it could do. His financial troubles would soon be over, for who could refuse to manufacture this machine under his patent and pay him royalties? At last he would be in reach of the "independent fortune" that had been uppermost in his thoughts for the past six years!

At the Quincy Hall Clothing Manufacturing Co. in Boston, Howe sewed as many seams as were brought to him, and, in addition, he challenged five of the firm's expert seamstresses to a sewing race. Each girl had the same length seam to sew by hand, while Howe had five seams to stitch with his little machine. Sewing five times as fast, he finished his five before any one of the girls', thus demonstrating, once and for all, the great value of his invention.

But things didn't turn out the way Howe had hoped. Some of those who witnessed the sewing race said the machine would throw thousands out of work; others said it was too costly and complicated to be practical. So instead of an enthusiastic reception, Elias Howe received nothing but abuse and sharp criticism.

His great disappointment didn't end there. Howe returned to Cambridge only to find that George Fisher had canceled his contract. He had

taken Howe and his family into his home, boarded them for more than two years, and spent more than $2,000 on Howe's idea. That was enough for him. The partnership was at an end, and Howe had to move back to his father's home.

Undaunted by his hard luck, Howe decided to try to sell his machine in England, since there seemed to be no demand for it in the United States. A loan from his father took him and his family, as steerage passengers, to London, where one Thomas, an unscrupulous manufacturer in Cheapside, hired him at £3 per week (about $9.00) and offered him a £3 royalty for each machine. Things brightened up for a while, but not for long. In a few months Howe had made his machine adaptable for Thomas' business, but in return for this he received intolerable treatment. One April morning when Howe's patience was at the breaking point, an argument started, resulting in Howe's discharge. To make matters worse, Thomas kept on making Howe's machines without paying him any royalty, and there was nothing that Howe could do about it.

Because of the dampness and chill of London weather, Howe's wife became seriously ill, and his three small children had to be taken care of. On top of all this, he was penniless and a total stranger in a foreign country. Through the chance acquaintance of a coachmaker, he was able to borrow enough to make another crude machine (his fourth) and borrow enough on that to get his family home.

Back in New York at the cheapest Bowery hotel, after his wife and children had returned to his father's home

*The first Singer machine*

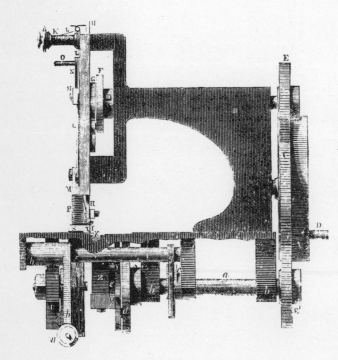

*Sewing head of
first Singer machine*

in Cambridge, Howe received the most distressing news of his career. His wife was rapidly dying of consumption, and he didn't have enough money to travel to her bedside. He finally borrowed $10 and was able to get to Cambridge just in time to see her die. This was by far the hardest blow, but Howe, with almost superhuman fortitude, weathered it along with all his other misfortunes. No longer was he a stranger in a foreign country, and he had many friends who cheered him and helped take care of his children.

Howe started to throw himself into hard work again on his fifth machine, when to his amazement he learned that a number of mechanics had been making sewing machines under his patent while he was away. The sewing machine had at last been accepted by the public, but Howe's name was never mentioned, nor did he receive any royalty from any of the machines. Though he was still a pauper, he resolved to prepare for war against these infringers. At first his father helped him financially, and a lawsuit was started; but as time went on, the legal expenses mounted up and Howe had to drop the suit. Howe then went to his old friend Fisher, who still had a half interest in the patent. But Fisher had had enough and refused to advance more money.

Howe searched around for someone to help him out of his difficulties and finally found a man by the name of George Bliss, who advanced the necessary money to carry on two lawsuits. Bliss had little faith in the machine and required a mortgage on the elder Howe's farm as security.

Most of the infringers were little mechanics who couldn't pay much if they lost, but there was one big fellow who had plenty of money, and it was on him that Howe concentrated. His name was Isaac Merritt Singer, a name famous throughout the world today as that of the pioneer manufacturer of the best sewing machines.

In the year 1853, after fourteen years of relentless struggle against intolerable misery and overwhelming discouragement, the wheels of fortune started turning the other way, and Howe began to collect on his invention. First the small infringers lined up with him and paid him all due royalties; then three astute businessmen helped him fight Singer, and in July 1854 Howe received $15,000 from Singer for a license under the Howe patent. From then on, all was easy.

*Isaac M. Singer, father of the modern sewing machine*

# ARTICLES OF AGREEMENT

Made and concluded upon this eighteenth day of September One Thousand Fight Hundred and Fifty, between George B. Zieber and Isaac M. Singer of the City of New York and Orson C. Phelps of the City of Boston.

In the first place, the parties above named, have agreed and by these presents so agree, to become co-partners together in an improved Sewing Machine, to be called the Jenny Lind Sewing Machine, and to apply for a patent for the same.

And it is further agreed by the said G. B. Zieber, that for the purpose of making an experimental machine, he will furnish the sum of Forty Dollars, and if said machine is successful, whatever further amount is necessary to procure a patent for the same. If the experiment fails, said Forty Dollars shall be lost to G. B. Zieber. He, the said G. B. Zieber, also agrees to attend to the business of the said co-partnership, to assist in making sales of rights and machines, and to do whatever may be a mutual advantage to the whole.

Each party to this agreement shall have power to sell rights and machines, which sales shall be valid and binding as soon as the payment received shall be divided equally among the parties to said agreement.

Said Issac M. Singer further agrees to contribute his inventive genius toward arranging a complete machine, and to do everything in his power towards perfecting the work, and all improvements which he, the said Singer, may make on said sewing machine, during the existence of this contract, shall belong to and be the property of, the said parties thereto.

Said Orson C. Phelps further agrees, for the sum of forty dollars before named to employ his best mechanical skill in completing a Machine, which machines, when completed and successful, shall be sent as a model to the patent office at Washington, upon which to obtain a patent, and it is also agreed by said Phelps that he will not at any time during the existence of this partnership, engage in the manufacture or invention of any sewing machine, except the one belonging to the parties to this agreement, and it is also agreed that said Phelps shall have the exclusive right to manufacture all the machines sold by the parties to this agreement, at the same prices that would be charged by any other respectable manufacturer.

It is also agreed that the patent shall be applied for an taken out in the name of Isaac M. Singer and Orson C. Phelps - but that said patent shall be the equal property of the three partners to this agreement, each owning one-third thereof.

In witness whereof, we have hereunto set our hands and seals.

G. B. ZIEBER

ISAAC M. SINGER

WITNESS:

O. C. PHELPS

JAMES BAKER, JR.

*Copy of the agreement between Zieber, Phelps, and Singer in which only $40 was involved*

# The Singer Manufacturing Company,

### No. 34 Union Square,

New York, March 13 1873

I M Singer Esq
London

Dear Sir.

Enclosed herewith please find usual Reports for Febur. also memo of Profits & Dividends from 1863 to this date.

You will Observe that the Profits for year ending December 31. 1872 amounted to $5.048.130 $83/100$ Dollars. viz Five Millions & Forty Eight Thousand, One Hundred & thirty $93/100$ Dollars. which added to Surplus Decr 31 1872 makes Surplus $14.382.953 $33$ Capital Stock $500.000 Total $14.882.953 $33/100$ Dollars.

The annual meeting day will be Wednesday the 19" Inst. The annual Report will be forth coming

With much Respect, I am Yours Hugh Cheyne

*The earned profits of more than $5,000,000 23 years after an original investment of $40*

*Singer sewing machine, from an illustration published in 1853*

Howe was the complete master of all designs involving the use of certain basic principles—and no machine can operate without using these principles. As the popularity of the sewing machine grew, Howe's bank deposits increased to such an extent that upon his death in 1872 his estate was appraised at the incredible sum of $13,000,000.

Of course, no name in sewing-machine history is as important or well known as the name of Singer. To Isaac M. Singer full credit is due for the development of the sewing machine, not only as a household article, but as the vital tool of the garment industry. How many millions of sewing machines have been sold since I. M. Singer & Co. was first formed is anyone's guess, but the Singer sewing machine today is known and used in every corner of the civilized world. In view of this, it is interesting to investigate the early years of manufacture and see how the practical sewing machine got its start.

Isaac M. Singer was a very astute businessman as well as an excellent machinist. In August 1850 he was working on a wood-carving machine which he had just patented. At that time a number of sewing machines which Howe had patented and which were made by other manufacturers came into Mr. Singer's shop for repairs. Singer, upon seeing their clumsy workmanship, immediately suggested vast improvements, among which was the idea of the to-and-fro movement of the shuttle in a straight line. The matter might have ended there, had not a devastating fire destroyed Singer's shop and his wood-carving apparatus, leaving him practically destitute.

Remembering the machines that

had been brought into his shop and his improvements on them, Singer decided to build what he thought would be a good practical sewing machine. He gave his rough sketch to two men by the names of Phelps and Zieber to work out the first model. These two men invested the sum of $40 in the venture, and the first practical, workable, and efficient sewing machine was developed.

Later on, Singer made many other improvements and soon organized the firm of I. M. Singer & Co., turning out sewing machines in considerable quantities. It was at about this time that Elias Howe threatened to sue the Singer Company, but settled for $15,000 plus royalties.

As time went on, Singer perfected his machine to such a degree that the demand became enormous, and twenty years after Phelps and Zieber had invested $40 in the first model, they had realized over $5,000,000 in royalties.

## 5. The Story of Photography

**"NATURE'S IMAGES ON SILVER."**  A popular homemade toy at the turn of this century was the pinhole camera. It was nothing more than a cardboard box, blackened on the inside, with a rather large hole at one end and a cutout rectangle covered with tracing paper at the other end. The hole was covered with tinfoil, and a tiny pinhole was carefully made in the foil. When this pinhole was turned toward a brightly illuminated object, the

*The newest of a long line of Singer family machines. It is made to sew a straight stitch as well as zigzag stitching, which through the use of fashion discs is fully automatic in the performance of specified designs. This machine can be operated at a speed of 1,500 stitches per minute*

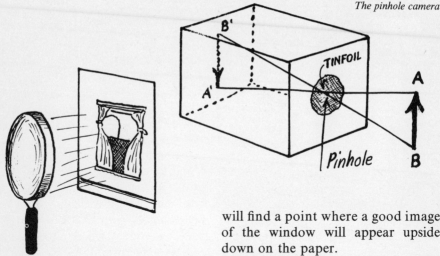

*The pinhole camera*

*Reading glass held near a window forms a perfect image of the window upside down on paper held behind the glass*

image of that object appeared upside down on the tracing paper.

This pinhole camera, in a more elaborate form, was popular in the fifteenth century. In those days they called it the "camera obscura," and it was used by artists to copy objects. All they had to do was trace the image that appeared on the ground glass, and they had a picture of the original subject. When the double convex lens became popular it was used instead of the pinhole and with much better results. In many cases the box became a large darkroom.

So, through a knowledge of physics and optics, men produced pictures on paper or ground glass by means of a lens. Anyone can do this by allowing the light from a window to pass through an ordinary reading glass and onto a sheet of white paper held about six inches behind the glass. By moving the glass or paper back and forth, you will find a point where a good image of the window will appear upside down on the paper.

But what good is a picture if you cannot keep it or reproduce it? The answer is found in chemistry rather than physics and might have been in the mind of Karl William Sheele, a Swedish chemist who in 1777 showed that a certain salt of silver decomposed when it was exposed to bright light. This important observation was followed up by Thomas Wedgewood, a young English lad who had done some experimenting with silver salts. Wedgewood, being extremely interested in chemistry, discussed the problem of light's effect on silver salts with the great chemist Sir Humphry Davy, and soon the two men were working together.

In 1802 Wedgewood and Davy coated a sheet of white paper with a solution of silver nitrate, placed some leaves over the sheet, and put it out in the bright sunlight. Where the shadow of the leaves fell, the paper remained white, while the parts of the paper that were exposed to the sunlight became very dark. This was the first negative; but the unexposed

*The camera obscura;*
*the ancestor of the present camera*

Nicephore Niepce and Louis Jacques Mandé Daguerre.

Niepce was born in Chalons, France, in 1765. As a young man he was somewhat impractical, without any marked ambition or interest in a career. Most of his time was spent with his brother, experimenting and inventing. After a long stay in the French Army, where he was rewarded for valor, Niepce became interested in printing from stone, a well-known art of that day. As time went on, he became more and more absorbed in this work, and in 1816 he started experimenting with the effects of sunlight on silver salts, just as Wedgewood and Davy had done many years before. Determined to make a picture that would remain fixed, he tried every conceivable method he could think of, but without success. For eleven years he labored in vain. Experiment after experiment failed, but Niepce never once became discouraged. With the rare tenacity characteristic of genius, he searched and searched, until in 1827 he learned of a resin known as bitumen of Judea, which was sensitive to light and at the same time soluble in an oil called essence of lavender. Niepce coated a glass plate with this resin and exposed it to the image from a lens in a camera obscura. Where the light struck the plate, it rendered the resin insoluble, and where it did not strike, the resin was soluble. By placing the plate in essence of lavender, he produced the first permanent *negative* in history. This was a fitting reward for genius.

parts, not being fixed, soon darkened when exposed to light, and the entire shadow picture became uniformly dark.

Someone suggested putting the treated paper in the camera obscura. It was obvious that a real picture would be produced on the paper instead of a silhouette. The experiment was tried, but it failed because the solution of silver nitrate was not strong enough to be affected by the dim image inside the camera. After many further experiments Wedgewood and Davy obtained reasonably fair pictures, but no matter how hard they tried they could not devise any way of making them "stay put." So, on the very threshold of one of the most important and valuable discoveries in the history of invention, Wedgewood had to admit defeat.

Photography, such as it was, stood still for twenty-five years while the world waited for someone to discover a method of fixing a picture permanently. In 1839 that method was found by two Frenchmen, Joseph

While Niepce's negatives were actually permanently fixed on the plates, they were quite impractical because of the extremely long and involved process required.

Two years after the triumph of the first negative, another Frenchman by the name of Louis Jacques Mandé Daguerre, a revenue officer, amateur artist, and scene painter in Paris, wrote to Niepce with the idea of collaboration. Daguerre had done a number of experiments in photography, and realized that he and Niepce could work together much better than he could alone. A partnership was formed, but unfortunately Niepce died before the ultimate triumph of the daguerreotype.

For seven more years Daguerre experimented and searched for a practical method of fixing pictures. Surely a process that required seven hours to make a picture of a landscape could stand improvement; otherwise it was doomed to failure.

By a happy accident Daguerre hit upon a process that eventually led to modern photography. He accidentally laid a silver spoon on a piece of metal that had been treated with iodine and noticed that the image of the spoon appeared on the iodized metal. This gave him the clue to the riddle. He exposed a highly polished silver plate to the vapors of iodine, which caused a thin layer of silver iodide to form on the plate. Silver iodide is extremely sensitive to light, so when Daguerre exposed the plate in the camera and removed it, the picture appeared as if by magic. The silver salt that was unaffected by light was dissolved away by a chemical suggested by Sir John

*A daguerreotype with the first human being ever to be photographed*

Herschel. This chemical was sodium hyposulfite, or hypo, which is still used today.

And so was born the first practical photograph of a scene. The first photograph of a human being was that of an unidentified man who stopped on a Paris street corner to have his boots blacked. If he had not remained still for so long, he would have vanished from the picture. The street seems to be deserted; but that is due to the very long exposure that Daguerre had to give the plate. This exposure was between ten and twenty minutes, so naturally all moving traffic would disappear from the scene. This picture is the turning point in the history of photography. It is remarkably clear, when you consider how crude the materials were and how little anyone knew of this new process.

On August 10, 1839, the French Academy of Fine Arts and the French Academy of Sciences got together to honor Louis Jacques Mandé Daguerre, the father of photography. Amid bands and cheers and flying flags it was announced that on that day a new art of daguerreotype photography was born, all because of the efforts and genius of the two men, Niepce and Daguerre, who discovered how Nature can "print her image on silver."

Great as the researches and discoveries of Niepce and Daguerre were, many other men of genius contributed improvements to the art at that time. While all the experimenting was going on, an English mathematician by the name of William Henry Fox Talbot was devising a method of reproducing photographs from a single negative. Talbot treated a sheet of paper with silver chloride and exposed it in the camera obscura just as others had done before him. Like the others, he obtained a negative on which the parts that should be white were black and the parts that should be black were white. By treating another sheet of paper in the same way and laying the negative over it and exposing them to bright sunlight, he obtained a positive which was the same as the original scene. He found that he could do this over and over again with the same negative and get as many positives, or real pictures, as he wanted. These pictures he called Calotypes, and later they became known as Talbotypes.

The progress of the photographic art may be approximately noted as shown in the table below.

And so photography progressed, and the entire world awoke to the possibilities it held. Opticians began experimenting, and all sorts of cameras were made, some large and some

| Process | Time Required | Introduced |
|---|---|---|
| Heliography .............. | 6 hours' exposure | ... 1814 |
| Daguerreotype ............. | 30 minutes' exposure | ... 1839 |
| Calotype or Talbotype ....... | 3 minutes' exposure | ... 1841 |
| Collodion process ........... | 10 seconds' exposure | ... 1851 |
| Collodion emulsion (dry plate). | 15 seconds' exposure | ... 1864 |
| Gelatin emulsion (dry plate) .. | 1 second exposure | ... 1878 |

small. Professional photographers sprang up everywhere just as spectacle makers had years before. As the demand for more and more daguerreotypes grew, scientists and inventors busied themselves on improving the art of photography. And photography certainly needed improving. In 1839, the year that it all started, there was no such thing as a photograph. What you got was a daguerreotype, which resembled our modern photograph only in results. To have your picture taken by this daguerreotype method you had to sit still for fifteen or twenty minutes in front of a huge cumbersome boxlike gadget on a tripod, while the pioneer photographer fiddled and fussed, one moment looking through the camera with a large black cloth over his head and the next trying to decide which bottle of chemicals he should use on his sensitized plate. It was an ordeal, and the results were far from satisfactory, in most cases a ghastly and insulting portrayal of the subject. In taking pictures of still life or buildings the daguerreotype was much more successful, as can be seen from the picture shown here; but the process was a newborn baby that needed constant attention and often produced no results at all.

In 1840 Pertzel, a professor in Vienna, made a camera lens that had excellent light-giving properties, and at the same time Professor John Goddard of London substituted silver bromide for silver iodide and was able to cut the exposure time from twenty minutes to fifteen or twenty seconds. This, of course, was a great boon to photography, especially in portrait work. But the most important improvement had to wait until 1847 and the discovery of collodion. Collodion is a very thin film of nitrocellulose, a distant cousin to cellophane, and when it is sensitized with silver bromide and poured on glass it makes a good photograph plate. This was known as the wet-plate process, a distinct improvement over all previous processes, yet quite impractical. A traveling amateur photographer who wanted to take pictures of the various places he visited would have to cart fifty or sixty pounds of equipment along on his back. He required a tent, a heavy tripod, a number of bottles filled with liquid chemicals, three or four trays, measuring glasses, stirring rods, a box of glass plates, and a great many tools, all in addition to a large and heavy camera. To take an outdoor picture would require anywhere from forty minutes to an hour of careful work, and the results were by no means sure to be satisfactory. This of course discouraged the amateur, so only professionals did any photographing in the field. The vital importance of collodion, however, was not in the results it got but in the new line of thought it started. It was the very beginning of film photography.

The next important step forward came in 1871 when the dry-plate process was invented by Richard Maddox of Woolston, England. Maddox produced the first gelatino-bromide dry plate, a dry emulsion on glass which was such a boon to photographers that amateurs started to use it. Among these amateurs was a young bank clerk by the name of George Eastman. Eastman took a keen interest in the photography of that time, but he

E.V.

didn't know too much about it. While he was telling a friend about his forthcoming vacation trip, a casual remark set off the spark that eventually enabled hundreds of millions of people all over the world to photograph anything and everything.

"George," said Eastman's friend, "why don't you buy a camera and have a picture record of your trip?"

The idea of a picture record of a trip fired Eastman's imagination. It was obvious that something had to be done to eliminate the bulky glass plates, heavy tripod, and camera if photography was to be a mass product, and George Eastman had visions of its becoming just that. He visualized people everywhere taking pictures of their trips as well as family portraits and records of growing children. The more he thought of it, the more enthusiastic he became, but to achieve this, machinery would have to be set up to produce negatives in quantity, and cameras would have to be greatly simplified and made much less expensive.

To do away with heavy cumbersome glass plates, Eastman experimented with gelatin and collodion but was unsuccessful. He finally tried celluloid and it worked. It could be rolled up and wound on a spool. It could be put inside a small black box with a shutter in front of the lens, and all one

would need to do was to press the button which would take the picture, turn to the next exposure on the film by means of a key outside the box, and take the next picture. One could get as many exposures on a single roll of film as he desired, and after all the exposures were made the photographer

*A wet-plate photographer and his materials. The wagon served as his dark room*

*George Eastman at the age of 36*

shutter and roll film was made in great quantity and sold for only a few dollars. He named it the Kodak, and all advertisements for this new Kodak carried the line: "You press the button, we do the rest." At last anyone, anywhere, could make good snapshots and have excellent pictures without knowing anything about photography. No more heavy and bulky equipment. No more fussing around with developers.

The demand for Kodaks spread all over the world, and Eastman was snowed under with orders. Everywhere people were "pressing the button" and letting Eastman do the rest. And now amateur photography has become one of the nation's leading hobbies and has created a business running into hundreds of millions of dollars a year.

could send the roll to a professional photographer and have it developed and prints made. What an idea this was! Fortunately, Eastman was no impractical dreamer. He was a man of action, so he started making just such a small box camera and searching for just the right kind of film.

Eastman started his own business in 1884. He hired a chemist by the name of Henry Reichenbach to work on a preparation that would give him a sturdy and durable sensitized film. It took Reichenbach five years to find the answer, but when he did he patented the process and gave it to the Eastman firm. From that time photography grew so fast that Eastman could hardly keep up with its progress. The little box camera with the

**THE MOVIES.**    It all started in 1824 when Dr. Peter Roget read a remarkable paper to the Royal Society in London. He explained how human vision persists in the form of memory for a split second after the scene has disappeared, and went on to suggest that, if a number of successive phases of the same scene were quickly flashed in front of the eyes, the memory would carry over from one picture to the next, and the result would be a moving picture.

Among the many scientists to study Roget's discovery was a Dr. Joseph Plateau, a professor of physics at the University of Ghent, in Belgium. He became blind in his untiring efforts to apply theory to practice and create a moving picture. Plateau cut slits at regular intervals in a large disc and placed pictures in progressively different acts of motion between the slits. He then held the disc up to a mirror, looked through the slits at the reflection of the pictures in the mirror, and slowly rotated the disc. To his delight, the pictures came to life and actually moved. Plateau had not only produced the first movie, but, more important than that, he had confirmed Roget's theory of the persistence of vision with regard to moving objects.

It wasn't long before Plateau's wheel, which he called the Phenakistoscope, became famous. It was made to show all kinds of different motions. Some wheels showed a man walking or running, others a dog jumping or a girl dancing. They all delighted and entertained, but that is as far as they went. In 1833 Dr. W. G. Horner improved on the Phenakistoscope by placing the pictures on a long strip of paper and putting it into a large upright drum with slits in it. When Horner rotated the drum and looked through the slits he saw a much clearer moving picture, because of the fact that the slits moved in the opposite direction from the pictures, thus

giving an instantaneous flash to each picture. Horner called his gadget the Zoetrope, and it was patented in 1835. While it did show beautiful motion in pictures, it was nothing more than a very attractive toy, for there was no known way of projecting the pictures onto a large screen for an audience to see.

The very first moving picture to be thrown on a screen was the brain child of Baron Franz von Uchatius. He combined the magic lantern with Plateau's wheel and threw the image onto a screen. Since it was a continuous movie, it was not too satisfactory.

So the moving picture had to wait for photography to catch up with it. Before a moving-picture show could be given to an audience, thousands of pictures had to be photographed in succession and flashed onto a large screen at the rate of sixteen or more

*The first Eastman Kodak*

*A modern camera*

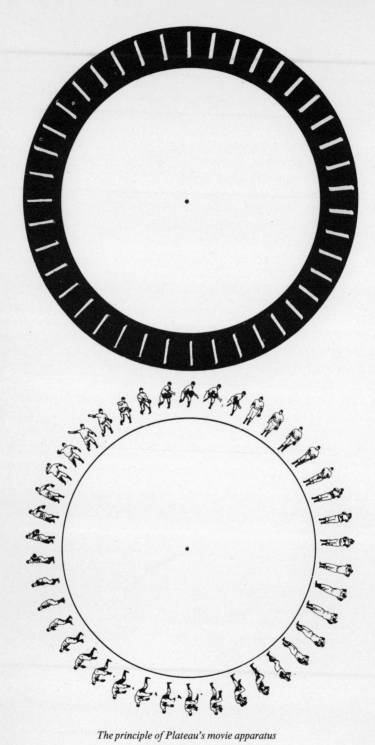

*The principle of Plateau's movie apparatus*

every second. But how could thousands of pictures be projected on a screen in such rapid succession when they were on glass plates, and when each picture took at least three seconds to make? For more than thirty-five years nothing was done to project moving pictures onto a screen. Photography was in its infancy, and there was no practical way of showing moving pictures to an audience.

In the early 1870's a seemingly unimportant incident occurred at a race track in Sacramento, California. Leland Stanford started an argument with a few of his friends concerning the manner in which a race horse ran. Stanford contended that there were times when a running horse had all of its feet off the ground at the same time, and the others said that was impossible. As the argument grew, bets were placed, and it was decided that the only way to prove the point, one way or the other, was to take photographs. As a great deal of money was at stake in this bet, the horsemen made up a fat purse and hired a well-known scientist by the name of Eadweard Muybridge to take a series of photographs of a running horse at extremely close intervals of time. This would settle the argument once and for all.

Fortunately for the hundreds of millions of moviegoers, Muybridge took his work seriously. To him it was much more than settling a bet for a few unscientific gambling men. In order to analyze the movements of a race horse he set up a couple of dozen cameras at regular intervals along the race track. Strings attached to the shutter of each camera were stretched across the track. As the horse galloped past, breaking the strings one by one, each camera took a separate picture. Each picture had an exposure of a fraction of a second, and when the complete set of pictures was developed, it proved beyond doubt that Leland Stanford was right—that there were times when a race horse had all four feet off the ground at once.

But Muybridge was not content with settling the argument. He saw the vast possibilities in the photographic study of motion, and became so fascinated with it that he wrote a book entitled *The Horse in Motion,* showing thousands of little photographs of horses in progressive stages of movement. J. B. Lippincott, the publisher of this book and something of a racing enthusiast, was so pleased with the results of Muybridge's researches that he financed him in other books on the subject of motion analysis. The outcome was a huge eleven-volume set containing more than a hundred thousand photographs of living creatures

*The Horner Phenakistoscope*

*Strip Kinetograph, a motion picture
machine made by Edison in 1889*

in motion. There were birds in flight, dogs running and jumping, athletes vaulting and racing and playing baseball, and all sorts of other forms of action.

The remarkable set of books on animal motion compiled by Muybridge had an enormous impact on moving pictures, even though the photographs did not move. Muybridge went to Thomas A. Edison and tried to get him to project his animal-motion pictures on a screen, so that they would actually move and a closer study could be made of them. Although Edison did not have any time to spare, he did realize that Muybridge had a wonderful thing, and in 1888 the Edison laboratories in Menlo Park, New Jersey, began to work on the kinetoscope. This was really a sort of peep show in which a few hundred excellent photographs flipped by on a large wheel, each one lit up by an electric spark for about a seven-thousandth of a second. The results were amazing. It

was the first time so many pictures had been put into one single moving picture, and by looking through the opening and turning the handle one could see a short playlet—the first movie dramas, if you can call them that.

Edison kinetoscopes were shown all over. People put in a penny and looked through the opening to see the first moving-picture show. But with all its fine mechanism and clear pictures, the kinetoscope could not *project* movies onto a screen. Edison produced the first practical moving-picture machine, but it was up to C. Francis Jenkins, in collaboration with Thomas Armat of Virginia, to invent the first projector enabling audiences to see a moving picture on a screen. To them goes the honor of inventing movies as we know them today. For producing "the first successful form of projecting machine for the production of life-size motion pictures from a narrow strip of film containing successive phases of motion," C. Francis Jenkins was awarded the Elliott Creson gold medal by the Franklin Institute of Philadelphia.

In the Jenkins projector a very long film with thousands of positive photographs on it moved across a projecting lens. In this Phantascope of 1894, the father of the modern movie projector, an electric motor turns a wheel rimmed with pegs to fit in holes on the edge of the film. As the pegged wheel, or sprocket, turns, it unwinds the film from the upper spool into the beam of light which throws the picture on the screen. The film, passing before the lens by jerks, stops only long enough to let each picture appear an instant on the screen, then moves quickly on, giving way to the next picture or frame. It is as simple as that.

In 1954 moving pictures celebrated their sixtieth birthday, and they certainly have grown in that time. One of the very first moving-picture projectors was the delicate-looking affair shown here. It was called the Vitascope and was first exhibited in New York in 1895. The pictures it showed

were pretty terrible, and the motion was even worse. They flickered and sputtered and jerked, but they did show photographs in motion. The public reaction was tremendous.

In 1903 and 1904 vaudeville houses all over the country gave variety shows, which usually included ten different numbers such as acrobatics, dialogues, songs of the day, and so on. People flocked to these shows as never before because they wanted to see Number 10, which was the Vitascope. The Vitascope performance usually lasted only two or three minutes, flickering out the motion of an approaching express train or a ride on a trolley car, with startling realism. Few inventions in history have met with such spontaneous and enthusiastic applause as the moving picture. Here people could see the pictures move right in front of their eyes, and they simply had to believe it.

Moving pictures made such a hit that the Vitascope started to enlarge its time and gradually encroached on the other numbers on the bill. The vaudeville actors, realizing this, began

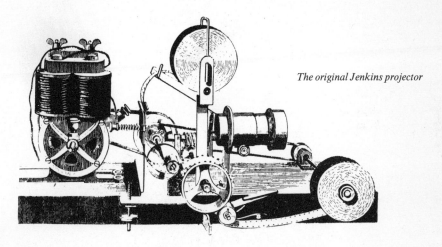

*The original Jenkins projector*

*Moving picture
attachment for a
magic lantern*

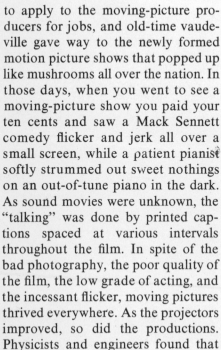

*Edison peep-hole
Kinetoscope of 1894*

to apply to the moving-picture producers for jobs, and old-time vaudeville gave way to the newly formed motion picture shows that popped up like mushrooms all over the nation. In those days, when you went to see a moving-picture show you paid your ten cents and saw a Mack Sennett comedy flicker and jerk all over a small screen, while a patient pianist softly strummed out sweet nothings on an out-of-tune piano in the dark. As sound movies were unknown, the "talking" was done by printed captions spaced at various intervals throughout the film. In spite of the bad photography, the poor quality of the film, the low grade of acting, and the incessant flicker, moving pictures thrived everywhere. As the projectors improved, so did the productions. Physicists and engineers found that

flashing twenty-five pictures per second, instead of sixteen, produced a much smoother and clearer motion. Then the quality of the film was improved, and in 1916 the Model E projector was introduced. This projector had all the latest improvements, including a new condenser lens and a much more brilliant arc light.

In 1926 moving pictures started to talk. Thanks to the vacuum tube of De Forest and the photoelectric cell (see Chapter VI, part 5), the first talking picture was presented on August 5 of that year at the Warner Theater in New York City. From that time on the motion-picture industry grew to giant proportions, ranking with other top industries in the nation. But the movies still had far to go. A good colored movie was a very rare thing in 1926, in spite of the first showings at the Rialto Theatre in New York in 1922. It wasn't until the early thirties that pictures in Technicolor could be seen everywhere. With perfection in movement, in color reproduction, and in sound recording, the moving-picture producers sat back and relaxed. How was it possible to improve on this? And then, shortly after the Second World War, came commercial television, and everyone everywhere was buying a set. This was a great threat to the movie industry, which had to offer something new and exceptional if it didn't want to lose its audience. And so Cinerama was invented, and with it came Cinema-Scope—the triumph of the huge screen. These innovations were promptly followed by three-dimensional pictures in Technicolor.

Cinerama opened its doors to the public in New York in 1952. Three projectors at equal distances from one another focus the same movie on a curved screen fifty-one feet long and twenty-five feet high. The center projector shows the same kind of picture that a standard machine produces: a direct view of the scene. The left and right projectors show what you would see if you turned your head slightly to the right or to the left. The curved screen, made up of hundreds of overlapping vertical strips, emphasizes this effect. The result is that your eyes are always conscious of what is going on to the right or left of them, even if they cannot directly observe the action. This idea captures vision as it really is. It enables you to "see out of the corner of your eye." By combining the three projections in this way, Cinerama produces a sweep of

*The Vitascope or Biograph*

vision never before seen on a movie screen.

Three-dimensional pictures, sometimes called 3D, have been known for a long time. Years ago the audience wore colored glasses with one red and one blue lens. Two films of the same picture, taken with a stereoscopic camera (a camera with two separate lenses set about the same distance apart as the human eyes) are superimposed on one another on the screen. The picture intended for the right eye is colored red, and the one intended for the left eye is colored blue. The result is that each picture enters the eye it is intended for, without being seen by the other eye, and you see things in relief just as you do in nature.

With Polaroid glass the older colored-glass system was replaced by a process that polarized the two films, one horizontally and the other vertically. The observer wears Polaroid glasses that combine the two pictures into one, the right eye seeing only the horizontally polarized picture and the left eye seeing only the vertically polarized picture. The effect is a perfect 3D picture in color. The disadvantage of this system is that one still has to wear glasses, as there is no known way of seeing 3D pictures clearly without them.

Cinerama and CinemaScope, while entirely different in their construction, are *not* 3D pictures, because *both* eyes see the same thing. From a psychological standpoint, however, there is a definite 3D effect because the screen is curved slightly and the observer, in viewing the pictures, not only sees what is going on in front of him but he also sees out of the corner of his eyes

*The modern projector*

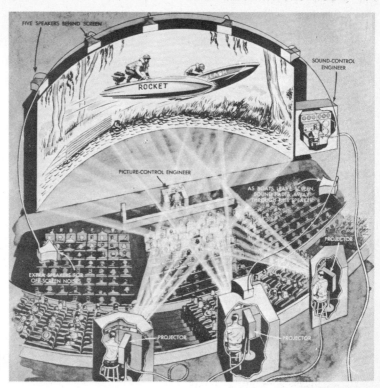

*Cinerama projection method*

and is conscious of things happening there, too, even though he cannot see them clearly. This is exactly what happens in actual vision and, in imitating this, the large movie producers have attempted the illusion of 3D without actually producing a 3D picture.

## 6. The Steam Engine

The first steam engine was built more than two thousand years ago by the great Greek scientist whom we met in Chapter II, Hero of Alexandria. It was totally useless from a practical standpoint and was exhibited in the Serapeum of Alexandria as a novelty.

Nobody, not even Hero, realized the importance of the principle behind this odd contraption, and it had to wait for more than eighteen centuries before men woke up to its enormous possibilities.

In the late seventeenth century two men, Thomas Savery and Thomas Newcomen, started experimenting with steam. Of the two, Thomas Savery is generally credited with the invention of the steam engine, even though his device was really not an engine at all.

Savery was a British sea captain who, while dining in a little tavern on the Cornish coast, noticed that a bottle partly filled with boiling water and allowed to cool sucked in its stopper as the steam from the water condensed. This gave him the idea that steam actually could move things, and in 1698 he made the first crude model of a so-called steam engine which had no moving parts and was of no particular use. In 1705 Thomas Newcomen, a British engineer, entered into a partnership with Savery, and together they produced a steam-powered machine that pumped water. It worked by the use of steam confined inside cylinders, with pistons which moved back and forth under the force of the steam.

The Newcomen engine, though an effective demonstration of the power of steam confined in a cylinder, was both clumsy and inefficient. Only a few of these machines were built, because the cost did not justify the results produced. It wasn't until 1783,

nearly eighty years later, that a British scientist named James Watt, while studying the disadvantages of the Newcomen engine, invented the flywheel, the sliding arm, and the valve. These three new additions to the Newcomen engine made the steam engine practical and efficient. Steam confined in cylinders forced a series of pistons to move back and forth. This motion connected with a sliding shaft which moved along a horizontal bar and turned a huge, heavy flywheel. The momentum of the flywheel not only helped to keep the pistons moving and allowed steam to enter and leave the cylinders at regular intervals, but it also could be used to furnish power to run machinery. The steam engine was thus put to many kinds of work, but it never occurred to Watt to use it for locomotion. Watt's engines were always stationary, but they had all the elements necessary to supply locomotive power.

*Cugnot's artillery tractor of 1769*

*Evans' boatlike steam carriage*

To James Watt, then, goes the honor of inventing the very first practical steam engine and introducing the nineteenth century to the age of steam. Although Watt was not the inventor of the locomotive, he was the pioneer whose marvelous invention eventually led to the locomotive which, for more than a century after its invention, was the chief mode of transportation in America and has done more to unite the United States than any other invention up to the dawn of the twentieth century.

As far as is known, the first self-propelled vehicle was constructed in 1769 by Nicholas Joseph Cugnot, a captain in the French Army, who designed it solely for the purpose of hauling heavy loads. This amazingly cumbersome contraption ran on three wheels and carried an enormous, heavy boiler and engine, both of which had to be moved every time the iron monster changed its direction. While it had little value as a means of transportation, it actually was, as far as we know, the first self-propelled vehicle.

Twenty years after the appearance in France of Cugnot's machine, a young mechanic by the name of Oliver Evans, of Newport, Delaware, took out a patent on what is considered the very first self-propelled carriage.

Evans applied steam at great pressure to a paddle wheel attached to the rear of a boatlike carriage and, at the same time, to a flywheel inside the carriage which, by means of a belt mechanism, turned the wheels of the carriage. This odd combination of steamboat and horseless carriage traveled on land about as fast as a man can walk and amazed all who saw it. It was called Orukter Amphibolos, and it, too, had little value as a means of transportation.

For some reason, Evans sent the drawings of this peculiar machine to England, where they were seen by chance by a brilliant British engineer named Richard Trevithick, otherwise known as "Captain Dick." Captain Dick, realizing the great possibilities of a self-propelled vehicle run by steam, started to do some inventing of his own, and in 1801 he came out with the very first practical steam carriage, which moved at almost fifteen

*Captain Dick's
self-propelled carriage*

miles per hour. Crude as this machine seems to us now, it actually did carry passengers moderately long distances and hence can be considered to be the great-great-grandfather of the automobile. Here is a description of how this first practical horseless carriage carried seven daring people over a high road in England:

"On January 1st, 1802, a party of seven with Captain Dick in charge, visited the home of Lord Dunstanville, but unfortunately it met with an accident and the carriage turned over. Luckily, nobody was hurt and while they were celebrating their good fortune, feasting on roast goose and wine in a nearby tavern, the water in the steam carriage boiled over, the iron became red hot and everything that was combustible burned to pieces, including the building in which the carriage was sheltered.

"Far from being discouraged, Captain Dick and his friend Vivian built another steam carriage and called it 'The Puffing Devil.' This, at a speed of eight miles per hour, got stuck in the mud and had to be overhauled. Later that year, it was run in the streets of London and probably caused the awakening of scientists to the possibility of the 'horseless carriage.' "

So important is this great-grandfather of the automobile that a complete description of it is well worth mentioning. The cylinders of the "Puffing Devil" were enclosed inside the firebox in the rear. The large wheels were ten feet in diameter, and each wheel moved independently of the others in turning. A pair of small front steering wheels was arranged to turn about a vertical axis and was manipulated by a handle bar. A brake was provided, as well as variable gears for changing speed and an automatic blower for the fire. The carriage had an elevated coach body, mounted on springs, where the driver sat.

In addition to being a pioneer in "horseless carriages," Captain Dick was the first man to build a steam engine that was to run on rails, a truly remarkable accomplishment which makes him the father of the locomotive and of the great railways of today.

In 1808 Trevithick built a circular railway in London. It was enclosed by a tall fence, and the public paid a shilling admission to see the steam circus and ride behind a locomotive. The engine was called the "Catch Me Who Can" and ran on rails.

Three years after the Trevithick engine appeared, John Blenkinsop built a coal-burning locomotive which propelled itself by means of a cog which engaged a rack attached to the tramway.

Many other locomotive pioneers followed Blenkinsop, all with the same scheme of a cogwheel method of locomotion. A new and revolutionary improvement came in 1815 when George Stephenson patented an arrangement for attaching the connecting rods to the driving wheels. This was an enormous step forward, since it did away with the gears and cogwheel tramway. Stephenson's invention enabled a locomotive to run on steel rails, propelled by the action of the connecting rods moving in and out and up and down with the two great driving wheels, and powered by the compressed steam in the piston boxes. In 1825 the Stockton & Darlington

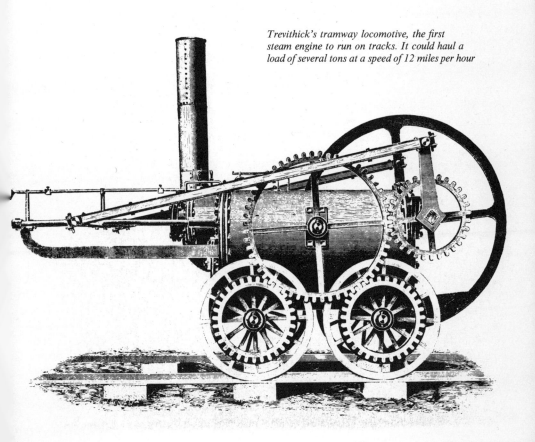

*Trevithick's tramway locomotive, the first steam engine to run on tracks. It could haul a load of several tons at a speed of 12 miles per hour*

# Early
# Steam
# Locomotives

*John Blenkinsop's cog-wheel
locomotive, 1811*

*The De Witt Clinton, first actual*
*train and engine to run in New York State*

*Thomas Rogers' first*
*locomotive, the Sandusky, in 1837*

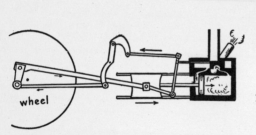
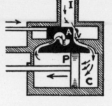
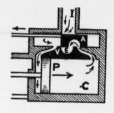

wheel

*The principle of the steam engine*

Railway in England was opened for traffic, with the Stephenson engine put permanently into service for hauling freight and carrying passengers. This was the very beginning of the era of the steam locomotive.

The principle on which a steam engine works is similar to the pump in reverse. It has a cylinder, a piston, and valves; but instead of being moved from the outside to pump out air or water, it is moved from within to create motion. A study of the illustration will make this clear. Steam under high pressure is admitted through the inlet pipe and enters the cylinder, pushing the piston to the left. As the piston moves to the left, one valve is closed by the arm and the other valve is automatically opened, allowing the steam in the cylinder to be pushed out through the exhaust. The heavy flywheel, of its own inertia, now pushes the piston back again and steam is admitted through the pipe again, since the first valve has now been opened. The same thing takes place all over again, and the piston, in moving back and forth, turns the wheel, which might be attached to an electric dynamo from which electricity is generated.

*An up-to-date "camel-back"
engine at the turn of this century*

*Giant New York Central locomotive of today. Weight 401,100 lbs.; speed, 70 to 80 miles per hour; 3,500 horsepower*

The piston box on an ordinary locomotive is the cylinder that contains the piston which moves back and forth, connected to the heavy flywheels of the locomotive by the piston rod. Enough steam entering this piston box will move the wheels of the engine and pull a heavy train of coaches. The steam is supplied from a huge boiler directly above the piston box. The exhaust steam is carried up the stack and out into the air together with coal dust and other impurities, otherwise known as smoke. By shortening the action of the valves in the piston box, a much quicker stroke is obtained and the engine is driven faster.

# CHAPTER V

# THE INTERNAL

# COMBUSTION

# ENGINE

The internal-combustion engine has changed geography by diminishing the vast expanses of the oceans, and it has whittled down travel time to such an extent that there is no place on earth more than sixty hours away from where you are. This amazing engine has made the nations of the world neighbors.

The automobile has changed our entire mode of living from that of our grandfathers' day. In the early years of the present century, people living in small villages had to depend entirely upon the old steam locomotive for traveling. In most cases they had to drive in a horse-drawn buggy over bumpy and rutty dirt roads to the nearest town in which there happened to be a railroad station. Today there is not a town or village anywhere in the United States that cannot be reached quickly and easily by automobile or bus. Dirt roads have disappeared and new four- and six-lane cement highways have taken their place. Cars go speeding along these highways at sixty or seventy miles an hour.

But the use of the internal combustion engine is not limited to motor vehicles. No farm of any size could exist without its motor-driven tractors, harvesters, threshers, and pumps. And think of the importance of this engine to building construction. Where would the giant bulldozer or the cement mixer or the derrick or the rivet hammer be without the gasoline motor?

The role played by the internal-combustion engine in air transportation cannot be overestimated. Because of it and the jet engine, Europe and the United States are only hours apart, and the valuable time saved by the airplane makes it the most practical and economical method of travel today.

## 1. The Gasoline Engine

The first engine that worked by the explosion of gas in a cylinder was made in 1820 by W. Cecil of Cambridge, England. He took advantage of atmospheric pressure and the explosions of a mixture of hydrogen and air to produce a continuous up-and-down motion of pistons inside a metal cylinder. He proved that if the explosions were regular, occurring at the rate of sixty per minute, of short measured amounts, they were quite harmless. His model of a gas engine, crude as it was, was acknowledged to be the first.

In 1823 Samuel Brown, an English scientist, made a number of improvements on Cecil's engine and succeeded in making the first commercially practical engine using gasoline as fuel. This engine was produced in quantity and sold in Croydon and other towns in England.

As the value of the gasoline engine became more and more apparent, inventors and engineers kept making improvements and inventing new methods of operating it. At the turn of the century it came into its own when Duryea used it for powering the horseless carriage and the Wright brothers used it in their first airplane.

It seems strange that practically all machines in the field of transportation are run by means of explosions.

An explosion is commonly thought to be such a destructive agent that it seems odd to consider it as a means of transportation, much less an enjoyable one. It is much more pleasant to think of cars run by silent electric motors or soft, hissing steam, but such cars have been tried and found to be impractical. An engine of this type must have quick and extremely forceful action, and the only way to get it is through continual rapid explosions.

Gasoline is explosive, but only when mixed with air. It is the mixture of the gasoline fumes with air, in the carburetor of the engine, that causes the explosions in the cylinders and sends the tight-fitting pistons inside them up and down. This up-and-down movement is transferred to a crankshaft under the car, and this crankshaft, through a system of gears, is connected to the rear wheels.

Now imagine four pistons inside four cylinders, as shown on the next page. They are all connected to a crankshaft in such a way that when the pistons inside cylinders 1 and 4 are moving down, those inside 2 and 3 are moving up. By alternating the timing of the spark plugs, which set off the explosions of the gas, the pistons will go up and down rapidly and

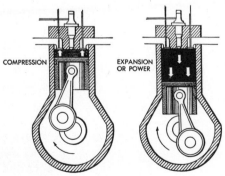

COMPRESSION    EXPANSION OR POWER

*The motion of the piston inside the cylinder. When the piston moves up it compresses the gas; then a spark ignites the gas and the explosion sends the piston down.*

produce a continuous turning of the crankshaft.

The gasoline is conducted from the tank of the car through the carburetor, which sprays it and combines its vapor with the air to make an explosive mixture. This explosive mixture is led into the cylinders, and as a result of the explosions set off by the spark plugs, the pistons are forced down the cylinders. The crankshaft is attached to a heavy flywheel, and the momentum of this heavy flywheel moves the piston up again after the explosions have lost their force.

Illustrated on page 103 are the four cycles for one complete movement of the piston. These four cycles are: (I) intake, (II) compression of the gas, (III) spark and explosion, and (IV) exhaust. This sequence is repeated many times every minute like this: intake, compression, explosion, exhaust, intake, compression, explosion, exhaust, etc., and the crankshaft keeps turning

and turning, and this constant turning gears into the rear wheels and causes them to keep turning. By adding more cylinders and timing the various strokes so that the piston in one cylinder will be moving *up* while the piston in the other will be moving *down,* we obtain not only additional power and speed, but smoother operation. The greater the amount of gas admitted through the carburetor, the faster will be the stroke and the faster the car will go. The same motion takes place in the Diesel engine shown on page 111.

## 2. The Story of the Automobile

Steam cars, around the turn of the century, were given a great deal of competition, because of a young man who had foresight enough to see the advantages of the gas engine. In 1890 Charles E. Duryea, while watching a crude, stationary gasoline engine at work, pumping away for all its worth,

*The crankshaft and how it is turned around and around by the movements of the pistons*

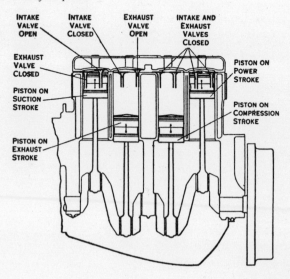

INTAKE VALVE OPEN

INTAKE VALVE CLOSED

EXHAUST VALVE OPEN

INTAKE AND EXHAUST VALVES CLOSED

EXHAUST VALVE CLOSED

PISTON ON POWER STROKE

PISTON ON SUCTION STROKE

PISTON ON COMPRESSION STROKE

PISTON ON EXHAUST STROKE

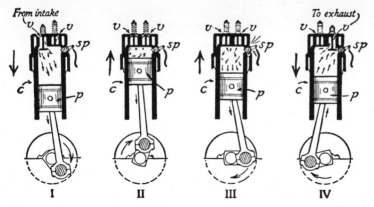

*From intake*

*To exhaust*

I        II        III        IV

*The four strokes of the engine*

decided that that kind of engine could be used to run a carriage. The next four years saw the building of many different models on which he and his brother, J. Frank Duryea, collaborated. The first practical horseless buggy, their fifth model, was completed a few years later and fitted out with pneumatic tires.

This gasoline automobile coughed and banged and thumped its way through the quiet, dignified town of Springfield, Massachusetts, in April 1892, much to the annoyance and amazement of the townsfolk. Horses shied, people gaped, and little boys ran alongside this self-running buggy. At times the carriage would get up enough speed to race bicyclists; at other times it would break down and refuse to budge, amid jeers of "Get a horse!" from onlookers.

At the turn of the century steam cars began to give way to the new gasoline motor, and during the next five years enormous strides were made in automotive manufacturing. That was a period of transition, of pioneer-

ing, and many names are identified with the development of those early cars. The inventive genius of men like R. E. Olds, David Buick, Elwood Haynes, Alexander Winton, and Henry Ford, transformed those first crude, noisy, rattling horseless buggies into a dependable, safe means of transportation.

One of these first cars was the Oldsmobile, manufactured by R. E. Olds in 1899. It was a buggylike contraption powered by a single five-horsepower gasoline engine having a top speed, on rare occasions, of eighteen miles per hour, or a little slower than a college sprinter can run. It is a curiosity today, and may be seen in the Smithsonian Institution in Washington, D.C.

In 1901 Olds produced and sold 400 cars, and the following year he turned out 2,500 but had a difficult time overcoming prejudice on the part of the public. Many considered the automobile dangerous and impractical, and the editor of a Louisville, Kentucky, paper wrote a seething edi-

*"Horsey Horseless Carriage" designed
by Uriah Smith of Battle Creek, Michigan, to
keep Dobbin from shying on the road*

torial about this monster that was terrorizing towns and cities and scaring people and horses alike. This editor also predicted that the fad for automobiles (which could be afforded only by the rich) would die out in a year or so.

But the fad didn't die out. On the contrary, people began to see the great advantage of the automobile over the horse-and-buggy, and it wasn't long before others started manufacturing cars of different designs. Among those were David Buick, who organized the Buick Manufacturing Company in 1902, and Henry M. Leland, who started the Cadillac Automobile Company that same year.

After another five years of pioneering, a buggy manufacturer in Pontiac, Michigan, realizing that the days of the horse-drawn vehicle were numbered, organized the Oakland Motor Company. He was Edward R. Murphy, and his cars were the first two-cylinder models capable of traveling up to thirty miles per hour.

On September 16, 1908, the General Motors Company was formed, and a year later Buick, Olds, Leland, and Murphy joined the organization. It was then that the automobile started to make strides.

Progress at first was slow. The cars were started by cranking; the driver had to turn the flywheel by hand in order to start the motor. This was a hard job because the flywheel was extremely heavy, and if it didn't turn properly it often meant a sprained arm. Another great obstacle to overcome in those early cars was the quality of the tires. Most of them were of a thin rubber which was very easily punctured by broken glass or nails on the road. Pumping these tires after fixing them with a gummy substance was a tremendous physical job, often requiring half an hour of exhausting work.

As time went on, better and more dependable cars were built. In 1909

*R. E. Olds's first horseless*
*carriage (steam), constructed 1886–87*

*The horseless buggy, one of*
*Charles E. Duryea's first vehicles, 1893*

*Hill's gasoline buggy*

*One of the first steam cars, built by
Dr. J. W. Carhart of Racine, Wisconsin, 1871*

electric headlights took the place of the old acetylene-gas lamps, and in 1910 the Fisher Body Company designed the closed body, a radical innovation in automobile design. In 1911 an old friend of Mr. Leland's was injured in the act of cranking a stalled car. Leland resolved to eliminate further occurrences of this nuisance, so he got in touch with Charles F. Kettering, a brilliant engineer and inventor who was experimenting with a self-starter. Kettering supplied Leland with his new gadget, which was installed with great success in the new 1911 Cadillacs.

Henry Ford was the one man most responsible for the development of the automobile, and no chapter on automotive history would be complete without an account of his remarkable achievements.

He was born on a farm near Dearborn, Michigan, in 1863. At a very early age he became fascinated by mechanics, and at sixteen he became an apprentice in a machine shop at $2.50 a week—seven ten-hour days.

Since his board and food cost him $3.50 a week, he made up the difference by working in a jewelry shop from seven to eleven in the evening at $2.00 extra per week.

Two years later Ford left the machine shop and went with a company manufacturing small steam engines, where he studied every motion they made until he could build one almost from memory. Ford's amazing mechanical ability enabled him not only to repair engines, but to improve on them, and it was only a short time later that he started building all kinds of engines.

After hours, he worked on a gasoline-propelled machine, completing it in 1892. This was his very first car—a two-cylinder, four-horsepower chain-driven contraption which he ran for 1,000 miles and then sold for $200.

By introducing to the country the assembly-line method of production, Ford was able to turn out cars by the millions, and in less than twenty years 15,000,000 cars of the old Model T were built. The famous Ford V-8 was

*Chassis and open body Cadillac of 1904*

*Oldsmobile of 1901*

*Buick of 1905*

*La Salle of 1928*

# Evolution of the
## Automobile Body

Cadillac of 1908

Cadillac of 1955

introduced to the public on March 31, 1932, and 5,000,000 of these were turned out in six years. Since its inception the Ford Motor Company has produced more than 35,000,000 cars.

## 3. The Diesel Engine

The Diesel engine uses air for its explosive mixture and certain kinds of oil as the "spark plug." It is a huge piece of machinery, and its enormous pistons are sufficiently powerful to compress the air in the cylinders to such an extent that the temperature of the air inside the cylinder is enormously increased. This is explained by Charles' law, which states that the volume of gas varies inversely with its temperature.

At 600 pounds pressure per square inch the temperature of the air inside the cylinder instantly rises to 1,000 degrees Fahrenheit. At this point oil is injected into the cylinder, and the extreme heat of the highly compressed air ignites the oil and sends the piston shooting up or down the cylinder with tremendous force. The inertia of this heavy mass of machinery brings the piston back to compress the air again and the same thing happens all over. The four cycles in the Diesel are similar to those in the gas engine.

## 4. The Story of Flight

THE AIRPLANE. From the earliest times man has wanted to fly. In medieval days he observed the birds, watching

*Giant 3-unit Diesel locomotive, 4,500 horsepower*

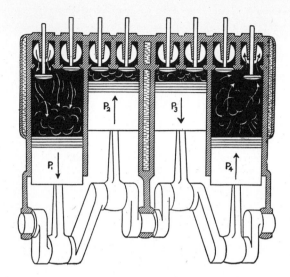

*The Diesel engine*

them flap their wings and soar gracefully into the air, and felt it was only natural to try to imitate them. It seemed so easy. Just build yourself a pair of wings, flap them, and off you go like a bird. Leonardo da Vinci had the first ideas about flying, but they were all impractical. Many an experimenter in the fifteenth century lost his life jumping off a roof and flapping a pair of wings. But what was wrong? A bird is not like a balloon; it is heavier than air, and yet it stays up by flapping its wings. So why cannot a man do the same?

This question was not answered until the year 1812, when Sir George Cayley, a brilliant Englishman, made a number of experiments with small models and discovered a few basic principles of aerodynamics. He demonstrated that birds never go straight up into the air when they start to fly. They start by flying very low and gradually gain altitude. This suggested to Cayley that rushing air had something to do with lifting the bird off the ground. He compared a bird with a balloon and showed the great difference between them. A balloon, being lighter than air, floats on air just as cork floats on water. It can stay suspended in the air for hours and not fall, because the gas inside the bag is lighter than the surrounding air. But if the bird stayed still it most certainly would fall, because it is heavier than air. It must, therefore, keep in constant motion, allowing the air to flow rapidly above and below its wings. The flapping of the wings is usually done as the bird starts out, and this is because the flapping creates the air currents so necessary for lifting. So any heavier-than-air machine must keep moving through the air if it is to stay up, and it must have something like the flapping of wings to create air currents. All these thoughts occurred to Cayley, who set

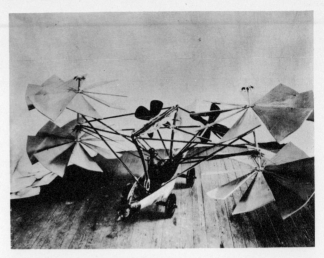

*Scale model of aircraft built from Cayley's 1843 drawings*

*A rubber band powered this model airplane, built by Penaud in 1871*

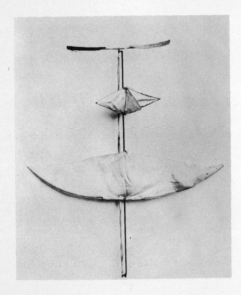

them down in a number of books which form the basis of aerodynamics.

While Cayley's models flew reasonably well, there was no way at that time to make a motor of any kind which would move blades rapidly enough and cause air currents. James Watt had just invented the steam engine, and Cayley thought of using it,

but he found it far too heavy and impractical. So Cayley died without being able to fly, little realizing the enormous contribution he had made to science.

The next, and by far the most important pioneer in early aviation, was the secretary of the Smithsonian Institution in Washington, an astronomer by the name of Dr. Samuel Pierpont Langley. He applied all of his mathematical experience and scientific skill to the problem of air currents and air lift, and it was undoubtedly he who first thought of using the principle of Daniel Bernoulli, a Swiss scientist, in the construction of the wings. This principle is so important that no plane could rise off the ground without applying it. Briefly stated it is: *when air is in rapid motion there is a decrease of pressure as the speed of the air increases and an increase of pressure as the speed of the air decreases.*

Dr. Langley decided that if the wings of an airplane were curved a little on top and flat on the bottom,

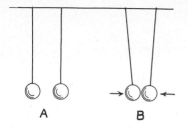

*Bernoulli's principle. Two apples are suspended from a bar by strings of equal length as shown in* A. *When they are at rest and entirely free from swinging, blow hard between them and immediately they will come together as shown in* B. *This is because the air current between them lowers the pressure of the air in that region and the pressure on the opposite sides of the apples forces them together.*

*Octave Chanute's glider, 1898*

the air, having to cover slightly more wing at the top than at the bottom, would have to do it in the same time. In order to do this the air above would have to travel faster than the air below, and according to the principle of Bernoulli the air pressure from below would therefore be greater and would lift the wing up. This vital principle is what lifts all planes.

Langley did a great deal of calculation on the construction of a man-carrying airplane, and on September 7, 1903, his machine, a hydroplane equipped with a home-built crude gasoline engine, was towed into the Potomac River at Tidewater, Virginia. The plane was launched against the wind with G. H. Manly, Langley's assistant and the builder of a gasoline motor, seated inside it. The engine started and the plane was ready to fly, but at the end of the track a post supporting one of the wings cracked, and the machine took a dive into the river. Neither Manly nor the plane was hurt. On December 8, 1903, Langley's plane was again tested, and again the same thing occurred. Greatly discouraged and out of funds, Langley had to admit defeat. Unfortunately, he gave up too soon. His plane never had a real chance. Glenn Curtiss took that same machine eleven years later (1914) and flew it successfully over Lake Keuka at Hammondsport, New York.

But Langley was not the only man who was experimenting with airplanes. Other names that appear on the pages of the history of that time are Lilienthal, Chanute, and Herring. Otto Lilienthal made a great many experiments with his large glider, eventually ending in a fatal crash. The two other men, Chanute and Herring, built odd-looking contrap-

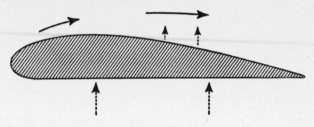

*All airplane wings are curved on top as shown here. Since the air has further to go on the top, because of the extra curve, it must travel faster than it does at the bottom, which is absolutely straight. Because of the extra speed of the wind or moving air on top, the pressure there is considerably lowered and the air from below pushes the wing up by Bernoulli's principle*

tions with many planes only to find them completely impractical.

The glider and airplane fever grew, and most youngsters, without knowing anything about aerodynamics, went in for making them instead of kites. Another craze was in vogue at the turn of this century: bicycles. Everybody was riding a bicycle, and that famous song about "a bicycle built for two" was the hit tune of the day.

In a bicycle shop in Dayton, Ohio, two brothers were discussing what they had read about the latest experi-

ments in gliders and airplanes. They were Orville and Wilbur Wright, who sold and repaired bicycles daily and made a fair living at it.

"Let's build a glider," said Orville to Wilbur. "We ought to be able to do a fine job with our mechanical knowledge." And so it was decided then and there on that summer day of 1900 that they would study up on all the past experiments of others and perhaps improve on them.

The Wright brothers soon became avid readers of every book on aeronautics they could lay their hands on. They not only read these books, they studied them, noting carefully the

*Lilienthal's odd-looking contraption*

*Herring's outlandish contraption*

*The Kitty Hawk, built by the Wright Brothers,*
*on its first flight, the first time man flew, December 17, 1903*

*The Wright biplane*

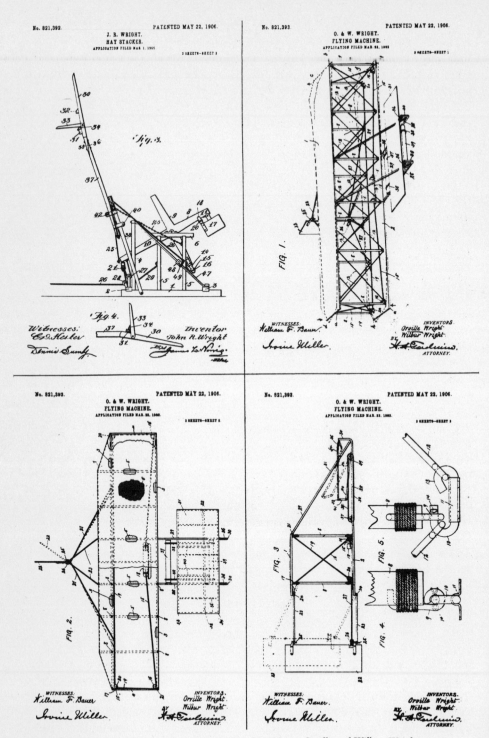

*The first patent on a practical airplane, granted May 22, 1906, to Orville and Wilbur Wright.*

mistakes that earlier experimenters had made and making notes for possible improvements. There were all sorts of difficult problems to solve, but they did not faze the brothers in the least. They kept on building and experimenting for the next three years. They made glider after glider, each one an improvement on the previous one, and all through this period they were both thoroughly convinced that they would be able to fly in a heavier-than-air machine.

But the public had a different idea. It was generally agreed that mechanical flights were impossible, and the U. S. Patent Office started rejecting, without examination, all applications for patents on mechanical flying machines. This seems truly amazing in the light of today.

After three intensive years of research and experiments with models in wind tunnels, the control problem was solved along with many others, and the Wrights decided it would be a good idea to install a gasoline motor in their next glider and test out their theories. This they did, and on December 17, 1903, at Kitty Hawk, North Carolina, just eight days after the failure of the Langley plane at Tidewater, Virginia, Wilbur Wright seated himself on the lower wing of his box-kite glider (equipped with a twelve-horsepower homemade gasoline motor and a propeller that had to be hand-started) and took off. The flimsy machine rose, and actually remained in the air for about twelve seconds. Greatly encouraged by this, the Wrights tried it again; and again their little plane stayed aloft, this time a little longer. At the fourth trial the plane actually *flew* nearly 900 feet in a minute!

At last man had conquered the air, and from now on he would be able to fly in a mechanically operated heavier-than-air machine. Just how far-reaching and vital to civilization this demonstration at Kitty Hawk was, nobody could possibly say. For the next three years the Wright brothers kept on making flight after flight, and by September 1905 they had extended the flight distance to several miles and had mastered many minor points in the control of the machine.

But still the general public was skeptical. Prejudice was very hard to overcome, and the man in the street as well as many scientists were still in the "show me" class.

It wasn't until the summer of 1909, when Louis Blériot, a French aviation enthusiast, made a successful flight over the English Channel in a little monoplane and won the *Daily Mail's* $1,000 prize, that the general public woke up to the possibilities of the airplane. This was an outstanding accomplishment at that time, ranking with the Lindbergh flight to Europe eighteen years later. Experimenters started building planes of every kind, and engineers worked on the development of the gasoline motor for use in the planes. The design of the propeller was improved; the assistant no longer needed to crank the propeller and run when it made the contact. Planes were equipped with wheels for taking off.

In 1910 there was so much interest and activity in airplane construction that England created the Advisory Committee for Aeronautics, which did an enormous amount of research in the testing of wing sections and improved design in plane construction. This was followed six years later by the establishment in America of the National Advisory Committee for Aeronautics, at Langley Field, Virginia. Here experiments were performed day after day on models in wind tunnels, and hundreds of trained engineers worked over drawing boards, designing new types of planes and improving the power of the motors. The science of aerodynamics grew rapidly, and aviation made enormous strides. In 1910 Glenn H. Curtiss made the first successful flying boat, or seaplane. A few years later he organized the Curtiss Engineering Corporation, which produced airplanes for commercial uses.

The First World War stimulated aviation. Airplanes were used to a large extent for reconnaissance purposes, and they proved very successful. After the war the first air travel was established. This was a service inaugurated on May 3, 1919, for carrying passengers from New York to Atlantic City, New Jersey. About this time air mail service was started. By 1924 pilots were carrying mail to all parts of the country on specified air routes, and it was then that a certain pilot got the idea of flying to Europe.

While air mail was now an established enterprise, commercial air travel was not. Too many people were reluctant to go shooting up a few miles in the air in a heavy machine, no matter how well it worked for the air pilots. And so it remained for Charles A. Lindbergh, an air pilot

captain, to prove to the world that air travel was safe and efficient. The rest is fairly recent history. Lindbergh's incredible accomplishment in 1927 electrified the world. If one lone man could fly to Europe in thirty-three hours in a tiny plane, certainly larger and more powerful planes with high-powered motors could be built to carry hundreds of passengers back and forth across oceans and continents at speeds double and treble the 100 miles an hour made by the "Spirit of St. Louis."

It would be wrong to say that Lindbergh was entirely responsible for the development of air travel as it is today. He merely blazed the way for others. Like the Wright brothers, he proved to a skeptical world that long flights over vast and dangerous areas are not only possible but highly desirable, since they can cut down travel time from days to hours. As a matter of fact, shortly after the Lindbergh flight Pan American Airways was organized, and a few years later, in 1934, large commercial planes were carrying passengers all over the nation at speeds up to 250 miles per hour. In 1939 the Second World War broke its fury on the world, and commercial planes gave way to bombers and jets. After the war enormous strides were made in commercial aviation, so that today we think nothing of stepping into a DC-7 at Idlewild Airport, New York, at 3 P.M. and stepping out of it at Le Bourget Airport in Paris sixteen hours later. This same trip would take about a week by boat, so the saving in time is positively astounding.

**THE PRINCIPLE OF THE AIRPLANE.** The two huge wings of an airplane are

*Blériot's monoplane, 1909*

*Latham's plane, 1909*

*Curtiss' biplane*

*Lindbergh's plane, The Spirit of St. Louis*

*DC-7 airliner. This plane flies up to 25,000 feet and has a maximum speed of 410 miles per hour. Its engines have 13,000 horsepower.*

tilted at a slight angle (about four degrees) to the horizontal, and they are considerably curved on top. The huge propellers are directly in front of the wings, and at the other end of the plane there is a very large vertical fin and a horizontal tail plane.

Before the plane takes off it is just like a bus with wings and a tailpiece. But as soon as the huge propellers start whirling at their enormous speeds and the plane gives a sudden lurch and in less than ten seconds is moving along the cement runway at eighty or a hundred miles an hour, you know the difference. And you also notice that you have traveled a considerable distance before you start to rise.

Now let us see the whys and wherefores of this procedure. Let us consider the propellers first, since they are the first to go into action. A propeller, whether it be on a transatlantic steamer or a huge transport plane, works on the principle of pushing or cutting the medium through which it rotates. If the propeller blades were absolutely flat there would be no motion whatever, because they would cut the water or air in exactly the same place all the time. The fact that the blades are curved slightly produces a motion in the water and in the air. If the propeller has four blades and each blade is turned up six inches, then one revolution of the propeller will send the boat or plane ahead four times six inches, or two feet. As the propeller

rotates with great rapidity, particularly in the case of an airplane, you can readily see how the plane can attain great speed.

Imagine a toy car on a toy track. On this toy car we place an electric fan. As soon as the fan is set in motion the car and the fan move, because the fan is blowing the air away from it and this action causes a reaction, moving the fan in the opposite direction from which it is blowing the air. Ordinarily the fan creates a wind but does not move forward or backward because the reaction is too small and the base of the fan is too heavy. When it is placed on wheels, however, the action of the fan blades on the air and the action of the air on the fan blades becomes equal and opposite, with the resulting backward motion of the fan.

An airplane is much like an electric fan on wheels. It is driven along the runway by these propellers, and since

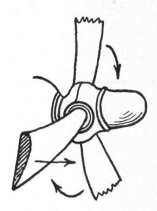

*Cut-away drawing of the airplane propeller. The curved blades stir up the air and plow through it at speeds depending on the speed of rotation.*

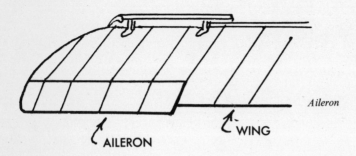

An electric fan produces a breeze because the blades push the air away from it. The fan does not move because it is far too heavy, but if it were put into a toy car on wheels on a track it would, by Newton's law of action and reaction, move the car while pushing the air.

AILERON    WING    Aileron

it is traveling so fast against the wind, the onrushing air not only strikes the undersurface of the tilted wings to produce a lifting force, but it also rushes over the curved tops of the wings, thereby lowering the pressure on the top by the principle of Bernoulli, as already explained, and increasing the pressure from the bottom.

The lifting force is enormous, and once the plane is in the air the four propellers keep it moving at speeds up to 450 miles per hour.

Now you can see how necessary the long runway is and how important it is to attain a very high velocity before leaving the ground. It is all a question of rapidly moving air striking specially designed wings head-on to lift the plane. The long runway and the high initial speed of the plane cause the wind to rush by the wings at an equally high speed.

The plane gains altitude by means of elevators and ailerons. The elevators are the rear hinged portions of the tail plane. They act in the same way a rudder does on a boat, only their movement is vertical and not horizontal. When they are depressed, the plane is steered upward; when they are raised, the plane is steered downward. The same action takes place in the ailerons, those hinged pieces on the wings. They are coupled

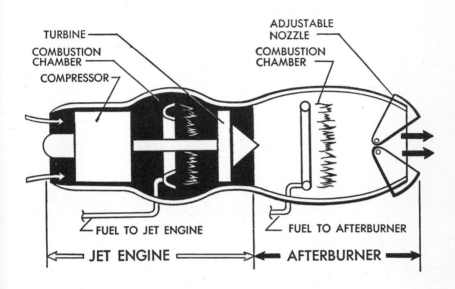

TURBINE

COMBUSTION
CHAMBER

COMPRESSOR

ADJUSTABLE
NOZZLE

COMBUSTION
CHAMBER

FUEL TO JET ENGINE

FUEL TO AFTERBURNER

JET ENGINE          AFTERBURNER

*The principle of the jet*

in such a way that when one is raised, the other is depressed. In this way one wing is raised higher than the other, and the plane tilts and changes its direction.

The landing gear of the plane consists of three pneumatic-tired wheels in shock-absorbent mountings, which fold up into the underside of the plane when it is in the air and slowly let down when the plane is about to land.

When about to land, the long hinged sections of the wings next to the ailerons are let down to catch the wind and reduce speed. As soon as the wheels of the plane touch the runway, brakes are applied just as they are in an automobile, and the plane is halted like any ground vehicle.

The airplane motor is an outstanding achievement in mechanical perfection. It is a twelve-cylinder liquid-cooled engine, and the method of power generation is very much the same as the four-stroke internal-combustion engine in the automobile, only very much more powerful. The gasoline used is known as high-octane gas, which is extremely flammable.

**JET AND ROCKET PROPULSION.** In the latter half of the seventeenth century Sir Isaac Newton propounded his famous laws of motion. The principle on which all jet planes and rockets are based lies in Newton's third law, which states that for every action

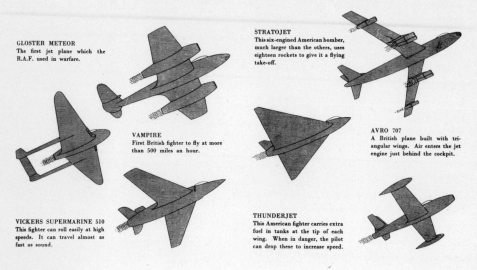

GLOSTER METEOR
The first jet plane which the
R.A.F. used in warfare.

STRATOJET
This six-engined American bomber,
much larger than the others, uses
eighteen rockets to give it a flying
take-off.

VAMPIRE
First British fighter to fly at more
than 500 miles an hour.

AVRO 707
A British plane built with triangular wings. Air enters the jet
engine just behind the cockpit.

VICKERS SUPERMARINE 510
This fighter can roll easily at high
speeds. It can travel almost as
fast as sound.

THUNDERJET
This American fighter carries extra
fuel in tanks at the tip of each
wing. When in danger, the pilot
can drop these to increase speed.

*Jet planes today*

there is always an equal and opposite reaction. A good illustration of this law is in the recoil of a gun when it is fired. The bullet, weighing little and traveling at a terrific speed for a long distance, causes the gun, which weighs a lot, to travel a very short distance in the opposite direction. Blow up a toy balloon, hold it at arm's length so that no air escapes, and then suddenly let it go. You will see the balloon dart out in a particular direction before it falls to the ground. The air rushing out of the balloon is the *action,* while the motion of the balloon in the opposite direction is the *reaction.*

Interest in jet propulsion started in England at the beginning of World War II. The design and development of the jet turbine is due to the tireless researches and experiments of Air Commodore Frank A. Whittle, an officer in the Royal Air Force. Whittle realized that a plane powered by a jet engine could fly much faster and higher than an ordinary plane and could thus be out of range of antiaircraft guns and make a speedy getaway after bombing. It also has many other advantages over the airplane, and Whittle succeeded in interesting his countrymen in its vast possibilities. In the early stages of the war the best engineering brains of England were put to designing and developing the jet engine. Today the jet is by far the most important airborne medium of defense.

Just as the gasoline and Diesel engines have their similarities and differences, so the jet and the rocket have theirs. In the jet and the rocket the method of propulsion is exactly the same—action and reaction—but the method of producing the force or action is different in each case. In the jet, air taken in at the front strikes the metal fins of a rapidly rotating fan.

This very fast rotation compresses the air, which is then led into a combustion chamber where it is mixed with kerosene in the same way that the carburetor of the gasoline engine mixes gasoline vapor with air. The mixture is then ignited and allowed to expand to an enormous pressure, after which it is shot out of the rear end of the plane. This terrific thrust of gas under great pressure, rushing out of the rear, pushes the plane ahead in the opposite direction just as fast. The two forces are equal and opposite; the gas forcing its way out one end and the plane forcing its way ahead in the opposite direction. By increasing the heat of ignition and the pressure of the gas, speeds of 800 to 1,000 miles an hour can be easily obtained. By building larger jets and using hotter gas, much greater speeds are possible. But there is one drawback to the jet: it cannot travel too far out in space, since it takes in air as it goes along and the farther out in space we get, the rarer is the atmosphere. And that is where the rocket has the advantage over the jet.

Unlike the jet, the rocket does not take in air as it goes along. It carries its own complete fuel system. This consists mostly of liquid oxygen, a very small quantity of which will produce a vast amount of the gas. Since it does not matter how little oxygen or air there is *outside* the rocket, it can travel far out into space where there is no air at all, and rockets have already been sent to heights of more than a hundred miles. There is little doubt that in the not too distant future huge rocket ships will travel thousands of miles into outer space, and possibly they will someday reach the moon. Whether any living beings will be able to survive such a fantastic journey is another matter, but certainly valuable information about the mysteries of cosmic rays and other phenomena of outer space will be had from the experimental journeys of future rockets.

# CHAPTER VI

# THE AGE OF ELECTRICITY

## 1. The Discovery of Electricity

It all began with an ordinary magnet and some amber and the brilliant mind and determination of Dr. William Gilbert. Dr. Gilbert, who was physician to Queen Elizabeth I of England, investigated the properties of lodestone and amber, and his work, published in 1600, is generally considered to be the beginning of the electrical age. The facts that a magnet attracted iron and that amber, when rubbed, attracted light bits of matter were known to the ancients, but no attempt had ever been made to fathom the mystery.

Gilbert was both fascinated and mystified by the behavior of these two common objects. A magnet was always a magnet, and it attracted iron and nothing else, while amber was not a "magnet" until rubbed, and then it attracted almost anything that was very light. Why should this be? After many years of experiment and research, the doctor produced the first comprehensive treatise on the theory of magnetism and magnetic attraction, and predicted that further experimenting with other substances like glass, hard rubber, sealing wax, and paraffin would ultimately result in the discovery of a new science, which he called electricity (the Greek word for amber is *electron*).

Dr. Gilbert's works attracted the attention of the scientific world, and physicists everywhere were soon probing the secrets of this new force. In 1729 Stephen Gray, another English scientist, made the startling discovery that electricity can actually be transmitted from one part of a substance to another. By means of a string attached to an electrified object he succeeded in attracting mustard seed at a distance of 700 feet from the source. He called objects which transmit electricity *conductors* and objects which do not transmit it *insulators*. A few years later it was definitely established that there were two kinds of electricity, which were ultimately called *positive* and *negative,* and a body was said to be *charged* with either kind. Charges that were alike repelled each other, while charges that were opposite attracted each other. This was the first basic law of electricity.

By the beginning of the eighteenth century it was a well-established fact that to electrify any insulator such as glass, hard rubber, amber, etc., brisk rubbing was always necessary, and the harder and more briskly the insulator was rubbed, the stronger would be the

travel down the metal bar and through the chain, which rests on the bottom. This fills the inside of the jar with negative charges and consequently drives all the negative charges on the outside of the jar down to the ground, since like charges repel each other. The outside of the jar is thus charged positively. The more charges that are sent into the jar, the more it will store them up the way a tank stores water. The capacity of this jar depends upon the amount of tinfoil and the thickness of the glass, and if a great enough charge is built up, the knob of the jar can become extremely dangerous because of the enormous shock it will release if touched.

The invention of the Leyden jar was an important milestone in the progress of electricity. Although unknown to the scientists of that time, it is also a *condenser* without which no radio receiving set or television set could work. The condenser, or *capacitor* as it is now called, is one of the most im-

*William Gilbert (1540–1603), who started it all*

charge of electricity. Instead of hand rubbing, electrical machines were made in which a wheel rotating very rapidly produced considerable friction. These machines not only produced strong electrical charges but the charges so produced could actually be stored up in specially designed glass jars, called Leyden jars because they were made in Leyden, Holland.

The Leyden jar is coated inside and outside with tinfoil and has a metal bar running down through the top, with a knob at one end and a chain at the other. The two metal surfaces are separated by glass, an excellent insulator, and the jar is charged by connecting the knob with an electric or electrostatic machine and connecting the outside of the jar to the ground. The charges that enter the jar

*The Leyden jar*

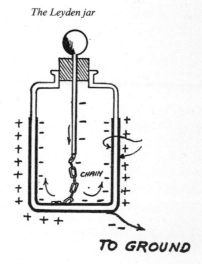

TO GROUND

*Benjamin Franklin (1706-1790)*

portant electric instruments today, but its value was completely overlooked until the famous experiments of Benjamin Franklin.

Franklin supposed electricity to be a sort of fluid. He argued that all bodies contain this fluid, but in uncharged bodies it produces no observable effect. The positive and negative charges neutralize each other. He suggested that a positively charged body contains more than a normal amount of this fluid, and a negatively charged body less than a normal amount. This theory is the basis of our present-day knowledge of the electrons and protons in matter, but in Franklin's day the inner structure of the atom was unknown. Franklin claimed that the atmosphere contains great quantities of electricity of the same kind that is developed from the electrostatic machines which charged the Leyden jars. He proved this in his famous kite ex-

periment in June 1752. He flew a kite during a thunderstorm, insulating the twine with silk ribbon. To the end of the twine he attached a key which sparked when the storm passed near and over the kite. As the twine was attached to a Leyden jar, the lightning charged the jar, thereby proving that lightning was the same kind of electricity as that which was formerly used to charge Leyden jars. It also proved that the atmosphere contains a great deal of electricity.

Up to the year 1760 only one kind of electricity was known, and very little was known about it. It was called static electricity—the kind that can be stored up in jars the way a housewife might preserve peaches. The vast potentials of the Leyden jar were still unknown, and the fact that varying the capacity of that jar caused sparks of varying wave lengths to fill all space with invisible electrical waves was undreamed of. Fortunately for civilization, electrical experimentation did not stop there.

Just twenty-eight years after Franklin flew his kite, Luigi Galvani of Bologna, Italy, while examining the muscular contraction of a frog's legs under the influence of the electric spark, accidently discovered the basic principle of *current* electricity. Galvani noticed that violent convulsions took place in the frog's legs every time a spark was produced in his electrostatic machine. What he had actually discovered was a means of indicating the existence and passage of a new form of electricity—the electric current. The frog's legs were, in a sense, a crude yet definite electric

# The Discovery of Current Electricity

*Luigi Galvani (1737–1798)*

*Galvani's experiment with the frog's legs*

*Alessandro Volta (1745–1827)*

meter, and Galvani, without realizing it at first, had found an entirely new and vitally important use for electricity. After more than six years of experimenting he erected an iron lightning conductor on the roof of his laboratory and connected it by means of copper rods to the nerves of a frog connecting the frog's legs to the ground so that the electric spark might travel through the body of the frog. Again the legs of the frog convulsed every time a flash of lightning occurred, and Galvani believed that these convulsions were due to the positive charge of the nerves uniting with the negative charge attached to the legs. He thought that both charges resulted from the decomposition of a natural source of electricity which existed in all animals. While this idea was wrong, it stimulated the imagination of Alessandro Volta, another Italian scientist, and enabled him to produce an electric current, for the first time in history.

Volta studied Galvani's experiment very carefully and noted that there were two different metals involved: copper and iron. Maybe the electricity flowed from one metal to the other, aided by the moisture of the frog's body. He followed this idea through by making a considerable number of discs of equal size from copper, zinc, and moist paper. He arranged a large number of these side to side in this order: copper, zinc, paper, copper, zinc, paper, etc. When he connected the first copper disc with the last zinc disc he felt a slight shock just like the kind that came from a charged Leyden jar. This was truly an amazing discovery. Electricity was produced without any rubbing of material on insulators, with no electrostatic machines, no amber or glass or magnets or anything else. Here was *an electric current generated entirely from the contact of two different metals and moist paper!*

Volta's discovery was immediately followed by a great controversy as to origin of the electricity. Nothing like this had ever been heard of before, and, though it seemed incredible, it actually worked. The only possible explanation was given by the chemists of that day, who suggested that dilute sulfuric acid be used instead of moist paper. The first voltaic cell, otherwise known as the first electric battery, was nothing more than a jar filled with dilute sulfuric acid and two strips of metal, one zinc and one copper, connected by a wire.

As more and more batteries were built and they became stronger and more powerful, the importance of Volta's discovery became apparent, and in 1801 Napoleon Bonaparte conferred the Legion of Honor and the Iron Crown upon Volta, who now is one of the immortals of science.

And so the second stage in the electrical age was born. Static electricity took second place, and current electricity became the most important subject in scientific circles. All kinds of batteries were made and tested and used in schools and colleges for the study and further advancement of electricity.

It is very strange to think of the world in 1800 as compared with the world today and to know that after a century of experimenting with electricity no one had yet found the magic key that would unlock the vast potentialities of electric power. The battery could run no motors because there were none to run. The battery could

not yet be used in the telephone or telegraph or radio, because all these electrical inventions had to await the greatest discovery of modern times. This discovery occurred twenty years after Volta's invention of the battery and was entirely due to the keen observation and brilliant imagination and foresight of a Danish professor of physics, by the name of Hans Christian Oersted. It was the linking together of electricity and magnetism into the new science of *electromagnetism* that changed the world.

The exact date of Oersted's experiment is not known. It was probably in the spring of 1820, for it was first announced on July 21 of that year. Oersted had been investigating electrochemical reactions for some time and was convinced that, just as an electric current can produce heat, so it can set up a magnetic field and influence the magnetic needle of a compass. It was his sole aim to prove this, and he had all the apparatus ready in his two front rooms on the third floor of Noerregade 34, Copenhagen, a kind of annex to the University of Copenhagen. After a lecture to his students he invited his class to witness what he and they little realized was the dawn of modern science.

Oersted's first demonstration was far from successful. Wire from a battery was placed in the immediate vicinity of a compass, but there was hardly any reaction on the compass

*The voltaic battery. Copper and zinc strips are connected by a jar of sulfuric acid and a current is set up in the wire*

Oersted's laboratory (arrow) at Noerregade 34, Copenhagen, where the world-shaking discovery was made. Reproduction of the original notes made by Oersted in his own handwriting. Out of these rough notes modern electrical science and engineering was born. Shown here is the original compass used by Oersted in his experiment. It has since been mounted on a wooden stand and is now in the Museum's physical laboratory in the Copenhagen Polytechnic Institute

needle. The students were unimpressed, and Oersted was disappointed but not discouraged. Being the genius that he was and having that deep conviction that he was right in his thinking, he kept on experimenting. A few days later he made a much stronger battery, and to his delight he observed a decided deflection of the compass needle as the wire from that battery was placed near the compass. But the deflection was not at all what Oersted had expected. When the wire was at right angles to the needle, there was practically no deflection, but when it was parallel to the needle, the needle swung around at almost ninety degrees. What was the reason for this strange behavior? And why did the needle swing to the *west* when the wire was *over* the compass, and to the *east* when it was *under* the compass? These were questions that had to be answered, and after countless experiments and infinite patience, Oersted not only solved the problems, but succeeded in producing and introducing to the world the fundamental principles of electromagnetism. He proved that the electric current in wires sets up a magnetic field around the wires.

The importance of Oersted's discovery of the relationship between electricity and magnetism cannot be overestimated. It is one of the most important discoveries of modern times. The fact that an electric current flowing in a wire produces a magnetic field in the immediate vicinity of that wire, and that the direction of flow governs the polarity of that field (whether it is positive or negative), not only led to the invention of the electromagnet, but it enabled Ampère to formulate the famous "motor rule" which is responsible for the invention of the electric motor. It paved the way for Michael Faraday and the first electric generator, not to mention quantities of electrical instruments and the comparatively recent invention of electrical transcription of sound, so important in the modern phonograph and in radio broadcasting. We shall see, when we discuss radio, how this magnetic field increases in intensity as the alternations in the current increase and how this increase produces the waves which make radio and television possible.

## 2.  The Story of the Generator, the Motor, and the Electromagnet

I have come home by subway from downtown New York to begin this section on the generator, motor, and electromagnet. The push-button elevator has taken me to my apartment, and I have just turned on the electric light. The night is exceptionally hot, so I turn on my electric fan. All this and hundreds of other uses of electricity I take for granted. I know it comes from powerful electric generators somewhere in the city, the whereabouts of which most of us neither know nor care. These faithful generators are continually humming and spinning hundreds of times every minute of the day and night, so that you and I and millions more like us can enjoy modern living.

Let us turn the calendar back a hundred and forty years or so, and visit George Riebau's little stationery and book shop on Blandford Street in London. It is the spring of 1812, and a

*Michael Faraday (1791–1867)*

customer is watching the young clerk and errand boy who is literally devouring *Mrs. Marcet's Conversations in Chemistry* and an article on electricity in an encyclopedia he is supposed to help bind.

Fortunately, the customer was no ordinary man. He was a prominent member of the Royal Institute of Science and was so impressed by the boy's interest in science that he started to question him. It wasn't long before he found out the quality of this youngster's exceptional mind, so he gave him a pass to four lectures on chemistry to be given by the great Sir Humphry Davy, the leading chemist in England.

And so, young Michael Faraday, the bookbinder's apprentice and son of a blacksmith, met Davy, who instantly recognized in him a budding genius and on the strength of that gave him a job in his laboratory. In a few months Faraday proved so valuable that Davy made him his assistant, and many years later, when asked what his most valuable discovery was, Davy replied: "Michael Faraday."

Oersted had proved that the current had a definite effect on the magnetic needle of a compass, so it seemed logical to assume that electricity and magnetism were bound together and that a magnet could be made to produce electricity. Faraday constantly kept in mind the fact that Oersted's compass needle changed its direction with the change of position of the wire. The north and south poles of the magnet must be influenced by the positive and negative charges of the current, so there was no question about the connection between the two. Faraday made hundreds of experiments with a coil of wire and a magnet, but they were all quite disappointing. Finally, on October 17, 1831, one of the most important days in the history of science, Faraday achieved his goal. Here is what he wrote in his diary that day:

" . . . A cylinder, hollow, of paper, covered with 8 helices of copper wire going in the same direction and containing the following quantities: 220 feet of wire separated by twine and calico. The internal diameter of the paper cylinder was 13/16"; the external diameter, 1½" and the length of the copper helices (cylinder) 6½". The outer casing was leather. The eight ends of the helices at one end of the cylinder were cleaned and fastened together as a bundle. So were the eight other ends. The compound ends were then connected with a galvanometer

# The Birth of the
# Electrical Age

## October 17, 1831

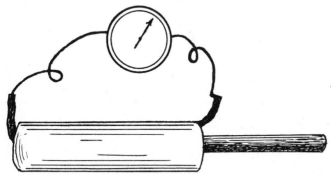

*Faraday's original experiment*

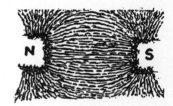

*Lines of force between the poles of a magnet.*
*Note how like poles attract and unlike poles repel.*

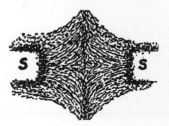

*The horseshoe magnet*

by long copper wires. Then a cylindrical bar magnet ¾" in diameter and 8½" long had one end just inserted into the helix cylinder—then it was quickly thrust in the whole length of the cylinder and the *galvanometer needle moved!* Then it was pulled out and again the galvanometer needle moved but in the opposite direction. This effect was repeated every time the magnet was put in and out and, therefore, a wave of electricity was so produced from the *mere approximation of the magnet* and not from its formation *in situ* [in place]. The needle

did not remain deflected but returned to its place each time." (See page 135, top.)

Imagine what a profound effect the success of this experiment must have had on Faraday. Here, for the first time, an electric current was produced without the aid of any battery or jars of liquid acid with zinc and copper poles connected from one jar to the other. Just keep moving a bar magnet back and forth inside a coil of wire and, presto, an electric current is produced. It was positively magic! Faraday, greatly encouraged by his

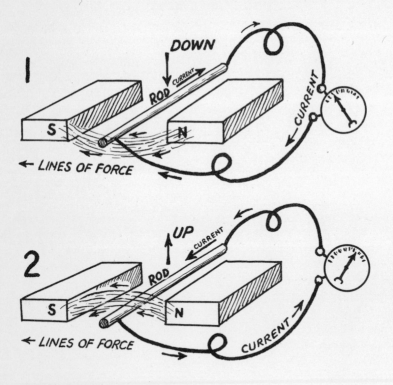

*Rod cutting the lines of force between the opposite poles of a magnet. In 1 the rod is moving down and current is going away from you; in 2 the rod is moving up and current is moving toward you*

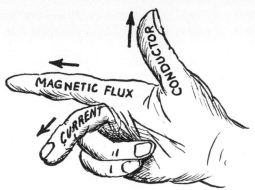

*The three-finger rule. Thumb shows direction of rod, fingers show direction of magnetic flux and current.*

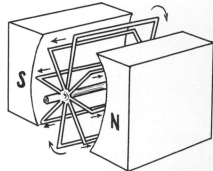

*Frame of metal conductors rotated between the poles of a large magnet. As rods move down on right, current flows one way; as rods move up on left, current flows in the opposite direction.*

discovery, decided that he could reverse the operation and get the same results. He could move a coil of wire up and down between the opposite poles of a horseshoe magnet, instead of moving the magnet inside the coil of wire, and the result would be the same. This he did, and a similar current resulted.

A discovery as vital as this naturally attracted considerable attention among the great scientists of that day. The cause of this phenomenon was investigated thoroughly, and after many more experiments it was conclusively proved that there exists between the opposite poles of a magnet a number of invisible lines of force because of the attraction of one pole for the other. These lines of force were made visible by covering the magnet with paper and sprinkling iron filings over it. It was known at the time that to overcome any force at all one must exert mechanical energy. But energy is indestructible, so it became quite obvious that in cutting these lines of force between the magnet's poles the energy required was transformed from mechanical to electrical, and that is why a current resulted. It was found that the faster the coils are moved and the more lines of force are cut, the greater the current.

During the next few months Faraday and the other scientists worked incessantly on the improvement of this principle, and so the very first crude dynamo was constructed. And from this dynamo the electric motor was born.

**THE PRINCIPLE OF TODAY'S ELECTRIC GENERATOR.** As we now know, if a coil of wire is moved up and down between the poles of a horseshoe magnet (see illustration on page 135), a small current of electricity will be set up in the coil. The invisible lines of force between the poles are cut every time the coil moves up and down, and the energy required to move the coil up and down, slight as it is, overcomes a certain amount of resistance and is transformed from mechanical energy to electric energy. The important fact is that only when the coil *moves* do we get current. If it is held stationary between the poles there will be no current at all. The force which creates the mechanical energy that moves the coil up and down many times a minute is turned into electrical force, and this electrical force is called *electromotive* force and designated by the letters EMF. In order to obtain a steady electromotive force, it is essential constantly to keep cutting the lines of force of the magnet. The stronger the lines of force are in the magnet and the more of them we can cut in a given instant, the greater will be the electromotive force we can develop from the generator.

Thus far we have been discussing a permanent magnet, which is very weak when compared with an electromagnet. We have also been discussing a small coil of wire which moves up and down by hand in a very crude manner. The resulting electromotive force in this case must necessarily be weak. If for the permanent magnet we substitute a powerful electromagnet with an enormously strong field (lines of force) between its poles, and if metal rods are substituted for the coil and dozens of them are moved by machinery up and down, cutting the powerful lines of force twenty or thirty times per second, the electromotive force that is developed will be many times greater.

In principle the electric generator is simple. The illustration on page 136 shows an ordinary rod cutting the lines of force between the poles of a magnet. As the rod moves down, a current is set up in the rod which moves in the direction of the arrow, and as the rod moves up, the current induced in the rod travels in the opposite direction. This is suggestive of the Oersted experiment in which the compass needle changed directions with the location of the wire from the battery. The flow of the current and its change of direction is important to remember, and it can easily be recalled by the three-finger rule. If your right hand is held as shown on page 137, the thumb indicates the motion of the rod (in this case it is up), the index finger indicates the flow of the lines of force (from north to south), and the third finger gives the direction of the current (coming toward you). Turn your right hand around so the back is toward you, and you will see the rod going down (the thumb is now pointing down); the flow of the lines of force is still the same, but the current is now moving away from you (the third finger is pointing away).

If now instead of a single rod we placed a number of rods on a frame or drum which rotates on its axis and we turned the drum very rapidly, the rods on one side would be moving up

# ALTERNATING CURRENT

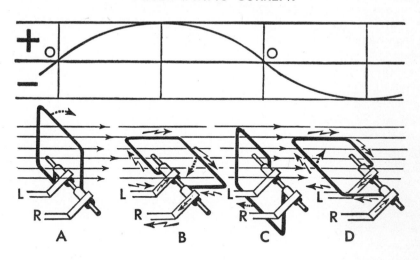

# DIRECT CURRENT

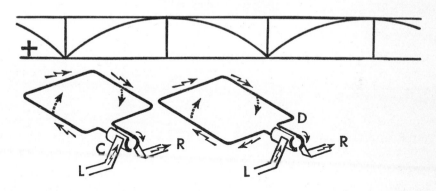

*The principle of AC and DC and the arrangements of the rings
or brushes which conduct the current away*

while those on the other side would be moving down. This rapid motion develops an electromotive force as we saw previously, and this EMF will be set up in the direction of the left side of the drum. Study of the illustration on page 137 shows that as this frame rotates there will be times when the rods will be moving in the same direction as the lines of force, and there will be times when they will be moving at right angles to these lines of force. This, of course, varies the intensity of the EMF in the rods. Obviously, when they are not cutting any lines at all, there is no EMF, and when they are at right angles to the lines, the EMF is at a maximum. This EMF is collected by metal brushes, as shown on page 139, and distributed through transformers over high-tension wires to communities where it lights the homes, runs the household gadgets and radios and television sets, and does a thousand and one other useful things.

In principle a generator is a large drum, called an armature, containing hundreds of small coils of wire, each separated from the next by a non-conductor and each lacquered to the drum and, at the same time, contacting the metal brushes, called commutators, at the axle. This armature is rotated at very high speed between the poles of a very powerful electromagnet called the field magnet, and a tremendous electromotive force is constantly generated. The power that drives the armature is usually steam or Diesel, but very often water power is used. Our great dams are used to generate power because the rushing water over the spillway has enormous energy, and this energy is used to turn the armatures of huge generators. This we call hydroelectric power, because it is motivated by water.

The type of generator we have described is an alternating current generator because it alternates from positive to negative sixty or more times per second. It is by far the most important current, as we shall see presently.

We see that alternating current (AC) results from an armature rotating in a magnetic field where the current varies from positive to negative many times per second, as shown

*Lines of force*
*between the poles of a magnet*

in the curve on page 139, top. In continuous, or direct current, the flow of current is one way all the time and resembles the lower half of the curve. In other words, in an alternating current the curve goes *above* the axis on the first half turn and *below* the axis on the second half turn. In a direct current, however, the curve always remains above the axis, and is always flowing in the same direction through the commutator. This is accomplished by means of a simple yet clever device known as a split-ring commutator. The current moving according to the three-finger law is moving away from you as the drum moves upward, and toward you as it moves downward. But, by means of the split ring, the two brushes rest on the opposite sides, so that each brush connects first with one end of the coil and then with the other end. The brushes are so adjusted that they shift just when the current in the loop is reversed. This produces a one-directional flow of current.

**THE ELECTRIC MOTOR.** An electric motor is the reverse of a generator. The generator requires mechanical motion from the outside in order to produce electrical energy. The force which turns the armature of the generator is usually Diesel power or water power. In other words, in the case of the generator we take advantage of water power or Diesel power to make electric power; while in the case of the motor we use the electric current which a generator has produced and turn that current into mechanical power for running our railroads, our factories, our mills, and all our electrical devices for the household, as well as for hundreds of other useful purposes in daily life.

If a copper wire is made to pass at right angles through a piece of cardboard on which are spread some iron filings, and if a fairly strong current is sent through the wire, a magnetic field is immediately set up in the vicinity of the wire, as shown by the pattern of the iron filings. It is important to note that the rotation of this magnetic field around the wire depends upon the direction of the current. This was first discovered by Oersted, as we already know. If the current flows in one direction, the magnetic rotation will be clockwise; if it flows in the opposite direction, the magnetic rotation will be counterclockwise. If you grasp a bar in the right hand, the thumb will indicate the direction of the current, and the fingers will indicate the direction of rotation of the magnetic field.

On the page opposite, we see the lines of force between the opposite poles of a magnet. They are undisturbed and flow evenly from the north to the south. In picture *1-c* on the next page we see a wire in section with the current flowing directly away from you. It is just as though a wire entered the page and went right through the book at right angles to the page. The circles indicate the direction of the magnetic field around that wire. In *2* in the full-page illustration we see this wire between the poles of the magnet. Now here is the important fact: The wire, having its own magnetic field around it, is also within the magnetic field of the magnet, because it is between the two poles. And the circular nature of the field around the wire is affected by the lines of force of the

# MOTOR RULE:

Current flowing in a wire sets up a magnetic field which distorts the original field of the magnet, making the original magnetic lines of force denser on one side of the wire and forcing it to move at right angles to the lines of force.

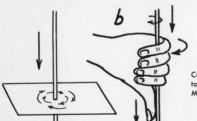

Current is flowing at right angles to this page and away from you. Magnetic rotation clockwise.

**1** a

Grasp a wire in the right hand as shown. The thumb points in direction of current and fingers show the rotation of magnetic field.

**2**

---

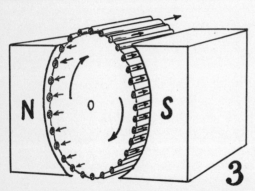

This shows a number of wires on a stationary drum between the poles of a magnet. AC current now flows through the wires, away from you on the right side and toward you on the left side. If you apply the right hand rule shown in 1b above you will see how the drum will be rotated, the right side is forced down and the left side forced up causing it to rotate rapidly.

**3**

---

**4**

### DYNAMO
**TRANSFORMS MECHANICAL ENERGY INTO ELECTRICAL ENERGY**

### MOTOR
**TRANSFORMS ELECTRICAL ENERGY INTO MECHANICAL ENERGY**

Coil A is made to swing between the poles of a magnet thus generating a small current which travels to coil B. As soon as there is current in B it will be attracted and repelled by the lines of force of B and will start to swing. Mechanical energy produced motion in coil A. This was turned into electrical energy in B.

**GENERATOR**

**MOTOR**

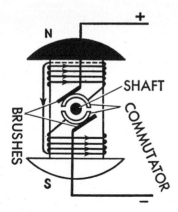

*The principle of the electric motor*

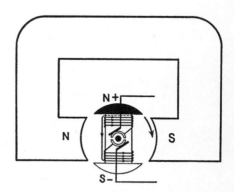

large magnet in such a way that the magnet is immediately repelled or at- tracted at right angles to these lines of force, depending upon the direc- tion of the current. This is known as a primary motor rule and may be stated thus: *A current in a magnetic field tends to move away from the side on which its lines are added to those of the field.* You can see from the illus- tration that when the rotation around the wire is clockwise, there is more magnetism going from north to south parallel to the magnet's lines of force than there is going in the opposite direction. Consequently, the wire is forced in the direction of the arrow.

In the motor we send a current through a series of wires around a drum or armature. The current flows from you on the right side and to- ward you on the left side. The rotary magnetic field set up in each of these wires causes them to move down on the right side and up on the left and

keeps the motor rotating as long as current is sent into it.

The principle of the electric motor may also be explained as follows: It is a fundamental law of magnetism and electricity that *like* poles or charges *repel* each other and *unlike* poles or charges *attract* each other. Two positive charges always repel, and so do two negative charges. A positive and a negative charge *always attract* each other. The same is true for the poles of a magnet. Bearing this in mind, suppose you had a large horseshoe magnet and you placed a small bar magnet between the poles of that horseshoe magnet so that the North pole of the bar magnet was close to the North pole of the horse- shoe magnet. And suppose that little bar magnet were pivoted on an axle so it could rotate, what would happen? The two North poles and the two South poles would repel and the little bar magnet would turn through half a revolution so that its South pole was near the North pole of the horseshoe magnet and there it would remain as shown in the diagram. But suppose that the instant it did this you made the poles of the little bar magnet change. The two North poles would be together again and so would the two South poles and the little bar magnet would turn another half revolution again. You can readily see that by making the two poles of the little rotating bar magnet change alternately from North to South, it would keep on turning and turning, always trying to find its opposite and always being repelled.

In principle the electric motor is a series of small electromagnets run by alternating current. These magnets are on a drum and they are arranged in such a way that the alternating current produces first a North pole and then a South pole many times every second. Since the two poles of the large magnet remain the same all the time, you can see that the wheel will rotate very fast, the magnets changing poles when they come near the opposite pole of the big magnet and hence are always trying to seek opposite poles and never succeeding, like dogs in a race running after that dummy rabbit and never catching it.

We have been talking about electromotive force and current as though they were one and the same. They are not the same and their difference may be shown in the following manner:

Suppose, instead of electricity flowing through a wire, we had water flowing through a pipe. The water will not flow unless there is a force to make it flow. The stronger the force that makes it flow, the greater will be a given quantity of water passing a given point in a given time. The flow of electricity in a wire is quite similar to this flow of water in the pipe. The electric current is defined as the flow of electrons from one point to an-

*Dynamo compared with a water pump.*

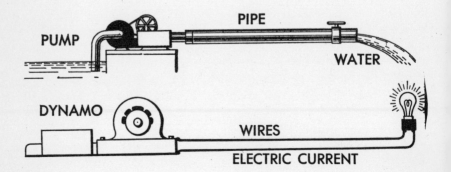

PUMP

PIPE

WATER

DYNAMO

WIRES

ELECTRIC CURRENT

*Joseph Henry (1797–1878), inventor of the
electromagnet, considered by many scientists to
be the greatest invention since the wheel*

*Henry's original electromagnet*

other. The greater the number of electrons that pass a given point in a second, the greater will be the strength of the current. This is measured in amperes, and one ampere is defined as $3 \times 10^{19}/4.77$ electrons per second. The force which "pushes" these electrons along the conductor is like the force which pumps the water through the pipe. It is the electromotive force, which is measured in volts. By rotating the armature of a generator at enormous speeds, a steady force is developed which "pushes" quadrillions of electrons per second out of the generator and on to the brushes. The increase in electromotive force obviously increases the strength of the current.

**THE ELECTROMAGNET.** The electromagnet is the invention of two men working independently: Joseph Henry, an American scientist who was the head of the Smithsonian Institution, and William Sturgeon, an English physicist. This little instrument is considered by many scientists the greatest invention of modern times.

The most common form of the electromagnet that we all use many times every day, yet which not one of us in a thousand ever sees, is simply a cylin-

*Samuel Finley Breese Morse*
*(1791–1872)*

drical piece of iron around which are wound coils of insulated wire. The iron is not magnetic when there is no current flowing through the coils of wire, but the instant, *the very instant,* that the current flows through the coils, the iron becomes a magnet whose strength depends upon the number of coils and the strength of the current. And the instant, *the very instant,* that the current in the coils stops, the iron loses all its magnetism. (See illustration on page 185.)

If the current went on and off a thousand times per second, the iron would become a magnet and lose all its magnetism a thousand times per second! And the magnet is so extremely sensitive to the slightest change or fluctuation in the current, that in the telephone it will not only

reproduce the very words you speak, but it will reproduce your voice, as distinguished from mine. Every tiny intonation and inflection is reproduced with uncanny accuracy in this little gadget whose reaction is instantaneous and whose sensitivity is infinite.

Just as the electromagnet can be made to reproduce any sound, so it can produce and control any mechanical motion at any desired distance. You can press a button in New York and start huge electric generators in Los Angeles; or a reporter in Chicago can type out the latest news in that city, and, thanks to the electromagnet, hundreds of Teletype machines all over the nation will instantly type out the same news exactly as the Chicago reporter types. If that reporter makes an error on his typewriter, the hundreds of Teletype machines will do the same, for they are all connected electrically with it, and the electromagnets in the machines in every city record exactly what they receive. When you dial a number on your telephone, many hundreds of tiny electromagnets go to work and connect you with any of the millions of telephones in the country. In the huge telephone building at 140 West Street in New York, more than 2,000,000 electromagnets in 10,-000 complicated frames handle the overwhelmingly complex communicating dial system for the three million telephones in that city. And it is all done instantly and with perfect efficiency (see illustration, pp. 178–179).

The electric bell, the push-button elevator and other push-button machines, traffic lights, railroad signals, and switches are all worked by electromagnets. The powerful generators that furnish the house current and light your homes, run your vacuum cleaners, make ice cubes in your electric refrigerators and do a-thousand-and-one other chores, are run by huge electromagnets. The electric motors that run our subways and streetcars as well as our large factories are a mass of electromagnets, and even the new science of nuclear physics, where atoms are split up by huge cyclotrons and betatrons, is entirely dependent upon huge, powerful electromagnets. There is no electrical invention today whose operation is not dependent directly or indirectly on the electromagnet.

## 3. The Story of the Telegraph

An art student at Yale, who later became famous as a sculptor and portrait painter both here and in England, is hardly the man you would think of as the inventor of the telegraph.

Samuel Finley Breese Morse, the son of a Congregational minister, was born in 1791 at Charlestown, Massachusetts. In his early years at Yale he did some experimenting in electricity under the able direction of Professor Jeremiah Day, one of the foremost scientists of his time. While science was by no means his forte, the idea of an electric current "flowing"

*Sketches from Morse's note book*

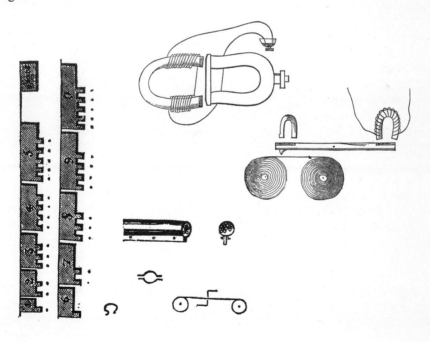

*The packet ship "Sully" on which Morse got the idea for the telegraph*

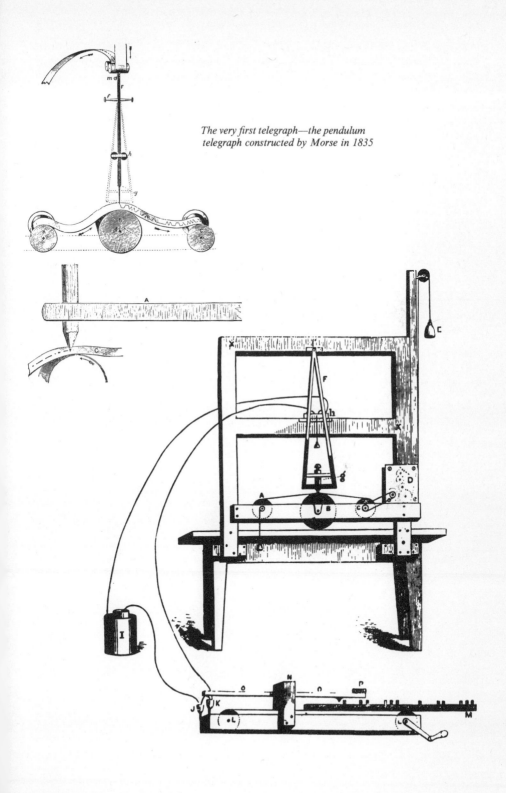

*The very first telegraph—the pendulum telegraph constructed by Morse in 1835*

through wires made a great impression on young Morse. Later in his life he remarked that it was "this crude seed which took root in my mind that ripened and possessed me completely after my trip from Europe."

It was in England that he made the acquaintance of some of the most notable artists of the day, and it was not long before his own paintings were hanging in the galleries of the Royal Academy. In 1815 he returned to the United States, where he found that his fame had preceded him.

Morse made his home in New York, where he and other artists formed the New York Drawing Association, of which he was president. During the next decade his art and lectures brought him such fame that he was elected first president of the National Galleries, a great honor well earned. In 1829, shortly after the

*A model of the pendulum telegraph shown on page 149*

*An early model of the
first practical telegraph*

death of his wife, Morse sailed for Europe again to study classic art in Florence, Rome, and Paris, without the slightest inkling of the surprise that destiny had in store for him. He was an artist and knew little about science. It is doubtful if he ever gave it a thought since his college days in the laboratory with Jeremiah Day, and he certainly wasn't thinking of it now. For three years he studied and worked long hours, acquainting himself with the world's greatest art masterpieces, and then at the age of forty-one, far out in the Atlantic Ocean, his entire life changed!

The packet ship "Sully," sailing from Le Havre to New York on October 1, 1832, carried many passengers, among whom was a Dr. Jackson who had been investigating electromagnetism in Europe. The large group of people who sat at the dining table the second night out from Le Havre were listening attentively to Dr. Jackson, who was explaining the wonders of the new electromagnet and the recent experiments of André Ampère, a French physicist and electrical theorist.

Dr. Jackson gave a rather long lecture on the electromagnet, explaining the importance of coils of wire. The more wire used around the coil, the stronger will be the attractive force of the magnet when current is sent through the wire. He was interrupted at one point by the question: "Is the speed of the electric current retarded by the length of the wire in the coils?" Dr. Jackson replied emphatically that the electric current passes instantaneously over any length of wire no matter how long. At this point Morse said: "If the presence of electricity can be made visible in any part of the circuit, I see no reason why intelligence may not be transmitted any distance instantly by electricity." The conversation went on, but the one new idea had taken complete possession of Morse. This was the turning point in Morse's life and, for that matter, the lives of everyone else in the civilized world. In those five words, "the electric current is instantaneous," Morse found himself back

| a | . — | 1 | . — — . |
| b | — . . . | 2 | . . — . . |
| c | . . . | 3 | . . . — . |
| d | — . . | 4 | . . . . — |
| e | . | 5 | — — — |
| f | . — . | 6 | . . . . . . |
| g | — — . | 7 | — — . . |
| h | . . . . | 8 | — . . . . |
| i | . . | 9 | — . . — |
| j | — . — . | 0 | —— |
| k | — . — | . | . . . — . . — . . |
| l | —— | , | . — . — |
| m | — — | ? | — . . . — . |
| n | — . | ! | — — — . |
| o | . . | " " | . — . . — . — . . . — |
| p | . . . . . . | ( ) | . — — . . — |
| q | . . — . | & | . . . . |
| r | . . . | | |
| s | . . . | | |
| t | — | | |
| u | . . — | | |
| v | . . . — | | |
| w | . — — | | |
| x | . — . . | | |
| y | . . . . | | |
| z | . . . . | | |

The Morse telegraph code,
not the International Morse code

in that physics laboratory with Professor Day and the "flowing" electric current. "If electric current can flow from here to any other part of the world in less than a second," thought Morse, "the current could be interrupted and a spark made to appear. The spark shall be one sign; its absence another; the time of absence still another. Here are three signs to be combined into the representation of figures or letters. They can be made to form an alphabet. Words may thus be indicated. A telegraph, an instrument to record at a distance, shall be the result. Continents shall be crossed. This great and wide ocean shall be no barrier. If it will go ten miles without stopping, I can make it go round the globe."

As far as he was concerned, art was a thing of the past. The same unbounded energy and enthusiasm so characteristic of genius was now concentrated on one and only one thing —the desire to make an instrument that could send messages instantly to any part of the world. Overnight he resolved to devote the rest of his life to that end, for nothing else mattered.

During the rest of the trip Morse remained in his cabin away from the other passengers, struggling with problems and making remarkable progress, considering his extremely limited knowledge of science. No longer did figures and landscapes take up the pages of his sketchbook; from now on they were covered with drawings of parts of the new telegraph.

Morse worked incessantly to make a workable telegraph. The obstacles he had to overcome were enough to discourage the most experienced scientist, but they had absolutely no effect on Morse. With almost no knowledge of electricity and less mechanical skill, he kept trying one thing after another, only to find that everything he tried was wrong. At the end of three years, the little money he had saved was gone without anything to show for all his work, and he had to fall back on his reputation as an artist.

In 1835 the New University of New York was founded, and Morse was offered the professorship of art and design. He took the job because there was nothing else for him to do, and fortunately he became acquainted with Leonard Gale, professor of chemistry at the New University. Gale made many valuable suggestions to Morse, recommending that he study the new invention of Joseph Henry, the electromagnet, and how it was constructed. This Morse did, and out of sheer perseverance he constructed a little electromagnet which worked to a limited degree.

On a wooden table he nailed a wooden frame, and on it he mounted his electromagnet. A pendulum swung back and forth near this magnet, and each time Morse made and broke the

*Perfected Morse register with tape recording of dots and dashes*

circuit in the current, the magnet drew the pendulum toward it and released it again. Attached to the bottom of the pendulum was a pencil which made markings on a paper tape placed directly under it. The tape moved along from one roll to the other by clockwork, and the zigzag lines on the paper, caused by the magnet's influence on the pendulum, produced a very crude series of letter codes.

The thing actually worked, but Morse was by no means "out of the woods." The current from the electric batteries was far too weak to send the message any distance, so Morse invented the relay. The relay is nothing more than an electromagnet that can be operated to close the circuit on a new line from another battery, thus adding more power to send the message farther. By introducing a number of such relays, the feeble current from the original batteries can be sent a long distance.

Morse, now a man of nearly fifty, had spent more than six years on experiment and research, and all he had was a very cumbersome device that showed how messages could be sent over the wire. But he had nothing else. He was absolutely penniless, and his reputation as an artist was long since forgotten. At this point he met a young man by the name of Alfred Vail, who was sufficiently interested in the invention to put $2,000 in it for improvement, in exchange for a partnership. This was just what Morse

*The clicker telegraph that was used in all small stations on railroads (key, clicker, and relay)*

*Simplified diagram of the start-stop system*

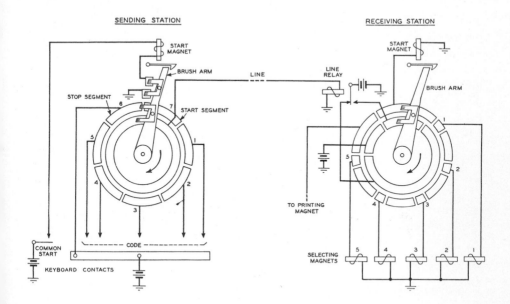

needed, and, with Vail's mechanical skill and the indomitable will of Morse, a workable telegraph was finally completed in January 1838 and introduced to the public.

The cumbersome contraption which was the first telegraph soon gave way to a more compact instrument run entirely by clockwork with no pendulum at all. Instead of zigzag lines, Morse made up the famous Morse code of dots and dashes, shown on page 152. The tape on this instrument was now marked with a dot or dash, and the code could be translated quickly. By means of relays and batteries of sufficient strength, this new device telegraphed messages over many miles, and the first real telegraph was born.

But nobody was interested. It was just some "newfangled idea" and an "impractical toy" to those who had the capital to invest. Not discouraged by this, Morse took the instrument to Washington, and with much convincing sales talk succeeded in persuading Congress to introduce a bill to appropriate $30,000 for the construction of an experimental line between Washington and Baltimore.

Encouraged by his success, Morse went to Europe to secure foreign patents, but again nobody was interested. The following year he returned to New York only to find that Dr. Jack-

*First teletype invented by Edison*

son, whom he had met on the "Sully" many years before and who had first introduced him to the electromagnet, had claimed a share in his invention. Not only that, but during the time he was abroad, Congress had cooled to the idea of the experimental telegraph, and the bill was temporarily shelved. This was the low point in Morse's life. The $30,000 that Congress was going to appropriate had become a myth; Jackson was claiming a half interest in his patent; and to make matters worse, Morse was completely destitute, so much so that at one point he actually faced starvation, with a total capital of only thirty-seven cents.

For almost a year Morse suffered, with nobody to turn to and no means of livelihood; and then on February 3, 1843, his bill for the $30,000 appropriation was again introduced in Congress; and this time, in spite of a great deal of ridicule, it passed by a narrow margin of only eight votes.

Success was assured. Morse and

Vail immediately started the construction work on the Washington-Baltimore telegraph line, but they foolishly decided to put the telegraph wire underground. This would have been all right thirty years later, but in 1842 the insulation was unusually poor, and defective wiring ruined their first attempt. After spending more than two-thirds of their money, they had to start all over again stringing the wires on crossbars nailed to poles spaced about a hundred feet apart and using glass bottles for insulation. Early in the spring of 1844 the line was completed, and on May 24, 1844, the great demonstration took place. With Vail in Baltimore and Morse in Washington, "What hath God wrought?"—the first message ever sent over wires—traveled from Washington to Baltimore in one forty-five thousandth of a second. But all those who witnessed this remarkable accomplishment were unimpressed. There was nothing spectacular in that simple message, and many people were frankly skeptical that it actually had been transmitted.

The situation was saved in a most ingenious manner. The Democratic National Convention just happened to be in session in Baltimore on May 24, and James K. Polk was mentioned as a candidate for the Vice-Presidency but suddenly brought forward to the Presidential nomination as a "dark horse." This left the office of Vice-President open, and a candidate had to be chosen. The delegates nominated Senator Silas Wright of New York, and as soon as Vail heard of this he telegraphed the news to Morse in Washington. Morse handed the telegraphed message to Wright, who refused the nomination, and Morse sent back the refusal to Vail by telegraph in record time. This message was then handed to the delegates at the Baltimore Convention, who didn't believe a word of it. A committee was sent to Washington the next day to check on the news, and as soon as it was verified the entire nation woke up to the enormous value of the telegraph. From then on, it was smooth sailing for Morse and his partners.

In 1856 the Western Union Telegraph Company was organized, and telegraph lines were strung all over the country and even clear out to the Pacific Coast. The profits piled up, and Morse and his partners, who controlled the patent rights, made a sizable fortune. Two years later the duplex telegraph was invented, an improvement on Morse's single system. J. B. Sterns of Boston patented a system whereby two messages could be sent over the same line at the same

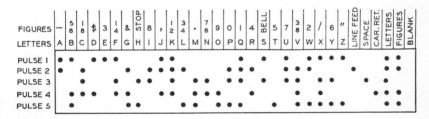

| FIGURES | - | 5/8 | 1/8 | $ | 3 | 1/4 | & | STOP | 8 | , | 1/2 | 3/4 | . | 7/8 | 9 | 0 | I | 4 | BELL | 5 | 7 | 3/8 | 2 | / | 6 | " | LINE FEED | SPACE | CAR. RET. | LETTERS | FIGURES | BLANK |
|---|---|---|---|---|---|---|---|---|---|---|---|---|---|---|---|---|---|---|---|---|---|---|---|---|---|---|---|---|---|---|---|---|
| LETTERS | A | B | C | D | E | F | G | H | I | J | K | L | M | N | O | P | Q | R | S | T | U | V | W | X | Y | Z | | | | | | |
| PULSE 1 | • | • | | • | • | • | | | | • | • | | | | | | • | | • | | • | | • | • | • | • | | | | • | • | |
| PULSE 2 | • | | • | | | | • | | • | • | • | • | | | | • | • | • | | | • | • | • | | | | • | | | • | • | |
| PULSE 3 | | | • | | | • | | • | • | | • | | • | • | | • | • | | • | | • | • | | • | • | | | • | | • | | |
| PULSE 4 | | • | • | • | | • | • | | | • | • | | • | • | • | | | • | | | | • | | • | | | | | • | • | • | |
| PULSE 5 | | • | | | | | • | • | | | | • | • | | • | • | • | | | • | | • | • | • | • | • | | | | • | • | |

*Chart of 5-unit TWX code*

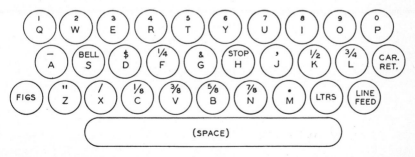

*Chart of TWX keyboard*

time. A message could be received at the same time and on the same line as a message sent.

Every railroad station had a telegraph office, and it was found that the tape method of dots and dashes was not as efficient as the "ear" method. The operator could tell the message merely by listening to the clicks. A short crisp click was a dot and a longer click was a dash. A special telegraph sounder was made for this very purpose, and for a long time all telegraphs operated on the sound principle instead of tape.

And so Samuel Finley Breese Morse, the distinguished painter and sculptor, was not only the first to produce a practical telegraph, but he had the honor of being the pioneer of most electrical communication in the world today, and the first man to make practical use of the electric current. True, Joseph Henry, the inventor of the first practical electromagnet, operated electrical telegraphs in his room in Albany in 1830, but he never patented his invention nor did he care to make practical use of it. He was only interested in the theoretical end of electricity and the further investigations of the works of Faraday and Oersted.

**THE TELETYPE.** The telegraph has undergone many changes since the days of the sounder which clicked out the messages in Morse code. The modern telegraph had its beginning in the laboratories of Thomas A. Edison. Edison, the most prolific inventor the world has ever known, was also a great improver on the inventions of others. It was Edison who as a youngster applying for a job at the Gold In-

dicator Company in New York saved a serious situation by fixing a telegraph in the office. In so doing, he not only got the job, but he studied the intricate mechanism and there and then decided to link the machine up with the newly invented typewriter. This resulted in the invention first of the stock ticker and then the Teletype machine, which is used today in every newspaper office in the world and which is the basis of the modern high-speed telegraph.

Edison decided that the dots and dashes of the telegraph could be turned into electrical impulses which, by means of electromagnets, could operate the keys of a specially designed typewriter.

Only five electrical pulsations control the working of the Teletype machine. In algebra, we learn that the number of ways of arranging two kinds of objects taken five at a time is $2^5$ or 32. The same holds true for these electrical pulsations. On the chart on page 157 you will see that each letter has a different combination of pulses. Letter $A$ is produced by pulses 1 and 2; letter $B$ is produced by pulses 1, 4, and 5; letter $C$ is produced by pulses 2, 3, and 4, and so on, all the way through the entire alphabet. This is the International Code used all over the world. Note that no two letters have the same combinations of pulses. Note also that since there are twenty-six letters in the alphabet and thirty-two combinations of pulses, there must be six pulses left over. These are vitally important and are shown at the extreme right of the code chart.

It will be noted that this keyboard is similar to the ordinary typewriter keyboard, except that there are only three rows of keys instead of four. In the typewriter keyboard the lower three rows of keys are used ordinarily for small letters, but when a shift key is operated they type the corresponding capital letters. The fourth or top row of keys carries the numerals and certain punctuation marks. The teletypewriter types capital letters but not small letters, so the upper-case position of the letter keys is available for the usual punctuation marks and numerals. Thus only three rows of keys are required on the teletypewriter keyboard. The operation of the figures key sends a signal causing the receiving machine to shift to upper-case so that numerals and punctuation marks will be printed until a letters or space signal is sent which restores the machine to lower-case.

The teletypewriter is so constructed that when a letter is pressed down it releases a little bar with teeth in it, and this bar makes a contact with one or more of the five copper plates which send pulsating currents through the telegraph wires to the many receiving teletypewriters in the various cities. This current enters one or more of the electromagnets in these machines and causes it to strike the paper. Take, for example, the letter A. As soon as it is struck on the sending teletypewriter, it releases a little bar with teeth 1 and 2 projecting down so that only contacts 1 and 2 are made with the copper plates and, consequently, the currents from plate 1 and plate 2 go out over the telegraph wires and enter the magnets 1 and 2 in the receiving teletypewriter, while plates 3, 4, and 5 are untouched and mag-

nets 3, 4, and 5 in the receiving machine do not act. The combination of magnets 1 and 2 in the receiving machine attracts a lever which, in turn, raises the A key on that teletypewriter and causes it to strike the paper just as though an operator were striking the A key. After the letter A is released the circuit is broken, and both machines, the sending and the receiving, move up one notch and wait for the next letter. Suppose the next letter is N. Referring to the code chart again, you will see that the letter N is produced by pulses 3 and 4. When N is struck on the sending typewriter, it releases a little bar with teeth 3 and 4 projecting down so that they contact copper plates 3 and 4 and consequently current from plates 3 and 4 (and no others) go out over the telegraph wires and into magnets 3 and 4 of the receiving teletypewriter. This combination attracts a lever which, in turn, raises the N key and causes it to strike the paper just as though an operator were striking the N key.

This is, generally, the fundamental principle on which the Teletype works.

**THE TELEGRAPH TODAY.** The illustrations on pages 161 to 163 show how the engineers of Western Union have built Morse's crude little machine into one of the most amazing communication systems in the world today. Many brilliant minds over the years have invented and patented vast improvements on the old Edison patents and now, as you can see from the photograph, Western Union has a machine that can send 3,000 words a minute to any part of the world.

Western Union engineers have been

steadily improving the telegraph since the days when it was just a sound-clicking instrument in every railroad station throughout the nation.

Today when you go into a Western Union office, the operator first types out your message on a Western Union blank and puts it in the Teletype machine shown in the picture. She then types the message on this machine, and you will note from the picture that it comes out on the left side on a narrow perforated paper tape. The perforations or code on this tape are exactly the same as those explained at the beginning of the section on the Teletype. As the tape passes through that boxlike automatic transmitter at the left of the operator, the coded symbols on the tape cause a photoelectric cell to flash the various dots, in the form of impulses, instantly to their destination. As previously explained in the description of the Teletype, these impulses energize electromagnets in the receiving machine, causing the particular letters of the typewriter to type out the message on a similar, narrow gummed tape which you can see coming out of the second machine in the picture. If you could examine both tapes, you would see that the sending one is a series of dots and dashes on plain paper, and the receiving one is your message typed out on a long strip of gummed paper.

The operator at the receiving end removes this tape and sticks it on a Western Union blank to be delivered to the party to whom you addressed the message.

The speed and efficiency of the Teletype system are amazing. There is no need to interpret the message from clicks of the Morse code, and the instant that the operator types the message on her Teletype, that message is typed on the receiving teletypewriter, all ready to be pasted on the Western Union blank. How proud Samuel Morse would be if he could come back now and see that crude early machine developed to such a remarkable degree.

The Western Union Company has also perfected the fastest telegraph in the world, known as the high-speed facsimile machine, which sends out words at the rate of 3,000 a minute. It can reproduce a facsimile of any page of typewriting, handwriting, or diagram, in thirty seconds. Transmission is so fast that two transmitters are used alternately, the one on the right to be loaded while the other is transmitting.

The facsimile machine, known as High-Speed Fax, works on exactly the same principle as the telephoto machine described in part 7 of this chapter. The copy to be transmitted is rolled and placed inside a long, transparent cylinder, so that the printed side is against the inside of the cylinder and may be seen through the cylinder. The cylinder is then rotated at a speed of 1,800 revolutions per minute, and at this enormous velocity the centrifugal force presses the paper tight against the inside of the cylinder, just as though it were glued there. A movable carriage containing a strong electric light and lens, together with a photoelectric cell, travels very slowly from one end of the cylinder to the other while it is in this rapid rotation. A narrow beam of light from the lens strikes the cylinder in the form of a

# Modern High-Speed Telegraphy

*HIGH-SPEED FAX, the world's fastest telegraph, can send words faster than you can talk—3,000 words a minute— 180,000 words an hour. High-Speed Fax can reproduce a page of writing or diagrams automatically in "picture" form in thirty seconds. Transmission is so fast two transmitters are used alternately. This permits one to be loaded while the other is transmitting.*

*A businessman is shown sending a telegram from his desk to Western Union's central office over a facsimile telegraph machine called Desk-Fax. Messages are sent and received automatically by Desk-Fax in facsimile "picture" form simply by pushing a button.*

# Modern High-Speed Telegraphy

*Operator on a modern Teletype typewriter.*
*Note the long strip coming from both machines.*
*The strip from the incoming machine (left)*
*is typed out already. This is cut up and pasted*
*on a Western Union blank to make the*
*telegram. The operator is typing a sending*
*strip to another office a few thousand miles away.*

small round spot. This spot of light is then sent through another lens, passes through a tiny opening, and is focused directly on the photoelectric cell.

You will appreciate the incredible sensitivity of the photoelectric cell when you consider that the typed page inside the cylinder rotates at the speed of thirty revolutions per second, and varying intensities of light and dark from the ink are sent through the narrow slit onto the photoelectric cell. To our eyes, at this speed, the result would be a continuous blur of gray, but the photoelectric cell picks up each individual ink mark and turns it into enormously rapid pulsations of current varying in strength according to their intensity. These electrical pulsations are sent by wire or amplified and sent by radio to their destination, where they are received and turned into a perfect facsimile of the orig-

inal picture or copy, by exactly reversing the process.

## 4. The Story of the Telephone

On pages 166 and 167 is a reproduction of Patent No. 174465, dated March 7, 1876, generally believed to be the most valuable ever issued in any language, in any country, and at any time. It is the final outcome of Alexander Graham Bell's search for a "harmonic telegraph" which would send musical tones electrically from one place to another. Most of Bell's previous patents (and there are many) show vibrating metal reeds under the influence of electromagnets as the current in those magnets varies in intensity. Bell figured that very rapid make-and-break circuits through the magnets would cause the metal reeds to move up and down so rapidly that they would vibrate and give out musical notes instead of the familiar click of the telegraph. But experiment after experiment failed to give the desired results; no make-and-break apparatus

*Edison's Telegraph Repeater, used to indent upon a sheet of paper the message in Morse code and to use that sheet as a record for sending the message to other machines in other cities. Edison found the germ of the idea of the phonograph in this recording machine.*

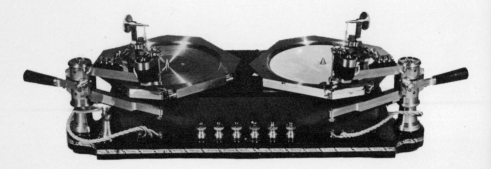

*Alexander Graham Bell (1847–1922)*

could be made to function satisfactorily at such a high speed, so Bell had to try a new device. Having an extraordinary knowledge of the human voice and the structure of the throat, he decided to substitute a stretched membrane in place of the metal reeds, and to use a liquid transmitter for his make-and-break circuit.

On the 10th of March, 1876, three days after this patent was issued, Bell and his able assistant, Thomas A. Watson, carried on their famous experiments in their rented loft at 5 Exeter Place, Boston. At one end of the loft was the room where Bell slept, and at the other end was his laboratory, a wire connecting the two rooms. On this particular day Bell was in his room and Watson was in the laboratory, far out of earshot. It apparently was a day of failure and dis-

couragement, and Bell was irritable and jumpy from loss of sleep and hours of hard work. It was while he was working with his liquid transmitter that, purely by accident, he upset the jar and spilled the weak acid over the table and on his clothes. In his consternation he exclaimed: "Mr. Watson, come here. I want you." Almost instantly the door of Bell's room burst open and Watson rushed in in wild excitement, shouting: "Mr. Bell, I heard every word you said—distinctly!"

This very commonplace sentence, now world-famous, was the very first to be sent over the very first telephone. Mr. Watson, in an address delivered before the Third Annual Convention of Telephone Pioneers of America, held at Chicago on October 17, 1913, said:

"It is hard for me to realize now that it was not until the following March that I heard a complete and intelligible sentence. It made such an impression upon me that I wrote that first sentence in a book I have always preserved. The occasion had not been arranged and rehearsed as I suspect the sending of the first message over the Morse telegraph had been years before, for instead of that noble first telegraphic message—'What hath God wrought?'—the first message of the telephone was: 'Mr. Watson, come here. I want you.' Perhaps, if Mr. Bell had realized that he was about to make a bit of history, he would have been prepared with a more sounding and interesting sentence. . . .

"Matters began to move more rapidly,

# A. G. BELL.
## TELEGRAPHY.

**No. 174,465.** Patented March 7. 1876.

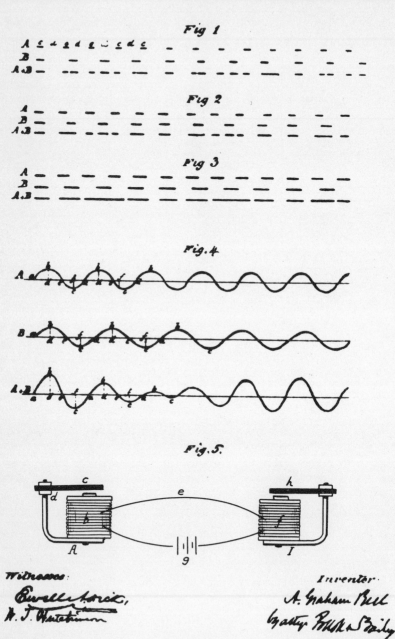

Fig 1

Fig 2

Fig 3

Fig. 4

Fig. 5.

Witnesses:

Inventor.

A. Graham Bell

A. G. BELL.
TELEGRAPHY

No. 174,465.

Patented March 7, 1876.

Fig 6

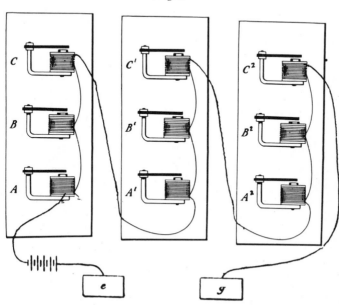

Fig 7

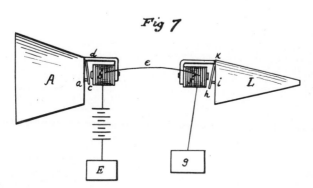

Witnesses

*Cuellerford*
*F. J. Hutchinson*

Inventor

*A. Graham Bell*
*by atty Pollok & Bailey*

*The most valuable patent ever issued—the telephone*

*Magneto wall set (Williams' coffin)*

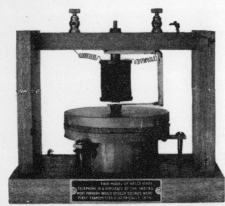

*Alexander Graham Bell's first telephone*

# The Early Telephone

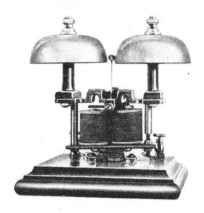

*Watson type of ringer*

*Model of the first commercial
telephone switchboard, used in New Haven,
Conn., in 1878 with eight lines and twenty-one
subscribers*

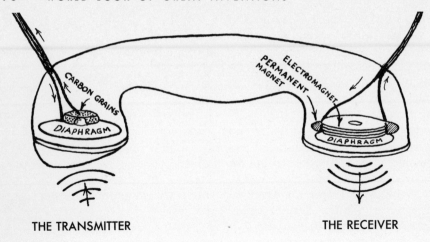

THE TRANSMITTER                                    THE RECEIVER

*Simplified diagram of
transmitter and receiver in modern phone*

and during the summer of 1876 the telephone was talking so well that one didn't have to ask the other man to say it over again more than three or four times before one could understand quite well, if the sentences were simple."

In 1915, two years after that convention, the first transcontinental telephone line was opened. Dr. Bell was in New York and Mr. Watson was in San Francisco, and before a large audience Bell repeated his words of nearly forty years before: "Mr. Watson, come here. I want you." Much to the amusement of the crowd, Watson answered: "I would be glad to come, but it would take a week."

It's quite a stretch from Bell's crude wooden instrument to the modern dial telephone. Edison and other great inventive and engineering brains have, over the intervening years,

transformed that first model into the greatest communicating network in history. In the United States more than 57,000,000 telephones and 700,-000 men and women handle and care for 200,000,000 calls every day in the year. So vast is the impact of Bell's invention on the world that it cannot be measured in money but only in terms of vital importance to every civilized human being today. Modern business is dependent on the telephone.

So perfect is the modern telephone that in 30 seconds or less you can converse with anyone anywhere in this country and hear him as clearly as though he were sitting next to you. Just think of how often you use the telephone, and you'll soon realize how you have been taking the wonders of this invention for granted.

Few people realize that network radio programs are telephoned from point of origin to the local radio stations that actually broadcast them. In order to link the nation's radio and television stations, Long Lines now operates about 160,000 miles of program transmission circuits. In addition to all that, Bell's basic patent, shown here, is responsible for the radio microphone and the loudspeaker, without which all radio and television sets would be silent.

**THE INVENTORS OF THE TELEPHONE.** This heading may surprise you. Everyone knows that Alexander Graham Bell was the inventor, but not many people realize that at least ten men before him had the same idea, and two of them made a workable model. One of these men was Philipp Reis, a German who, thirteen years before Bell took out his famous patent, made a crude model of a telephone which actually transmitted the voice as well as Bell's model did. That model is now in the Museum of Science in London, and a card next to it reads: "Original Reis Telephone, made by J. W. Albert, lent by the Institution of Electrical Engineers. This instrument, made in 1863, was invented by Philipp Reis of Frankfort for the transmission and reception by electrical means of all kinds of sounds and is generally held to be the first telephone." Apparently nothing was ever done to patent this invention, while Bell, working feverishly on his own investigations of rapidly vibrating reeds, discovered the principle of the phone independently and took out not one, but many patents.

Elisha Gray of Chicago on July 27, 1875, was granted Patent No. 166095 for the electrical transmission of sounds by telegraph. In later years Gray brought suit against Bell for in-fringement, but the court ruled in favor of Bell, since it was obvious that through his persistent efforts a workable telephone was produced, while Gray concentrated on transmission of tone.

Among the other men who had the idea for the telephone long before Bell are such men as: Farrar, Bourseul, Yeates, Varley, Cushman, Meucci, Petrina, and Manzetti. Bourseul's telephone, never patented, was worked out in 1854, twenty-two years before the Bell patent.

Alexander Graham Bell was born in Edinburgh, Scotland, on March 3, 1847. His father, Alexander Melville Bell, was a world-famous teacher of speech, author of many books on the subject, and inventor of Visible Speech, a code of symbols which indicated the exact position of the throat and tongue and lips when uttering various words and sounds. This system was used not only in schools of elocution but also as a guide and help for the deaf in learning to speak.

In 1866, while the nineteen-year-old Bell was examining a report of his famous father's experiments with vowel sounds, he came across a book entitled *Sensations of Tone,* by the great physicist Hermann von Helmholtz. The book was written in German, which Bell read with difficulty, and listed a number of experiments in combining electrically driven tuning forks to make vowel sounds. It was fortunate that Bell got the wrong idea from these experiments because of his difficulty with German. The book emphasized the importance of vibrating tuning forks, and the electrical part was incidental. Bell, inter-

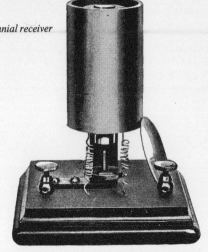

*Bell's original centennial receiver*

preting it as electrical transmission of tones, started thinking about sending tones by telegraph, and it was then that the seeds of the "harmonic telegraph" were planted in his mind. He already knew that sounds had been telegraphed over wires by using make-and-break circuits but thought he could improve this transmission by using vibrating forks or metal reeds.

It is interesting to note that as far as is known Bell had never made any far-reaching search on the idea of the telephone and knew nothing about the many men before him who had the same idea. He was not thinking of the telephone at first; he merely wanted to transmit tones by telegraph. But it was through his experiments that he developed the telephone. He died on August 2, 1922, in his summer home in Nova Scotia.

**HOW THE TELEPHONE WORKS.** The telephone consists primarily of a transmitter and a receiver. Inside the transmitter is a metal box, about the size of a small pillbox, filled with tiny, loosely packed grains of carbon and situated directly behind the mouthpiece. When you speak into the transmitter, the sound waves from your voice cause the air to vibrate. These vibrating waves hit the sides of the metal box and cause them to press, ever so slightly, against the loose carbon grains inside. That pressure, slight and imperceptible as it is, varies as the vibrations of the air waves beating against the sides of the box vary. An electric current is con-

stantly flowing through that box. It enters at one end and leaves at the other, and it passes through the carbon grains. The carbon grains conduct the current in exact proportion to their closeness to one another. The closer they are, the better they conduct the current; the looser they are, the worse they conduct the current. So the very slightest change in pressure on the carbon grains will be recorded by the very slightest change in current strength. Consequently, the vibrating metal box produces a fluctuating current which is really an electrical replica of the sound wave. This fluctuating current is sent to the central office, where it is switched by machine or manual means into the circuit with which you have asked to be connected. As soon as the circuit is completed, the phone you are calling rings. When it is answered the fluctuating current from *your* transmitter, caused by the vibrations from *your* voice, enters the other receiver.

Inside the receiver of the telephone

is a permanent magnet, at the end of which is a small electromagnet. Very close to both magnets, but not touching them, is a thin disc which is as free to vibrate back and forth as the sides of the metal box are in the transmitter. The permanent magnet exerts a steady pull on this disc, keeping it absolutely motionless. But see what happens when the fluctuating current enters the electromagnet. Bearing in mind its limitless sensitivity and instantaneous reaction, you can see that it will vary in strength in exact accordance with the variations in the current which enters it. These amazingly rapid variations attract and repel the metal disc that is so close to the electromagnet. When the current is strong, the disc will be imperceptibly attracted to the electromagnet in a fraction of a split second. When it is weaker, the next fraction of a split second, the disc will relax slightly. The metal disc in the receiver behaves in exactly the same way as the sides of the metal box behaved in your transmitter when you spoke into the mouthpiece, and, consequently, will cause the same vibrations of air to come out of the distant receiver as went into the mouthpiece when you spoke into it. The receiver, then, will reproduce your words and voice exactly.

**THE DIAL TELEPHONE.**    The dial telephone system is the most ingenious, efficient, and overwhelmingly complicated labor-saving device ever conceived by the mind of man. It is so vast in its complexity that it would require a course of intensive study to understand it fully and a book twice the size of this one to describe it in detail. If you glance at the photographs you will realize why it is impossible to explain everything about this system

*Telephone apparatus patented in 1876 by Bell, models made from figure 7 in Bell's original patent*

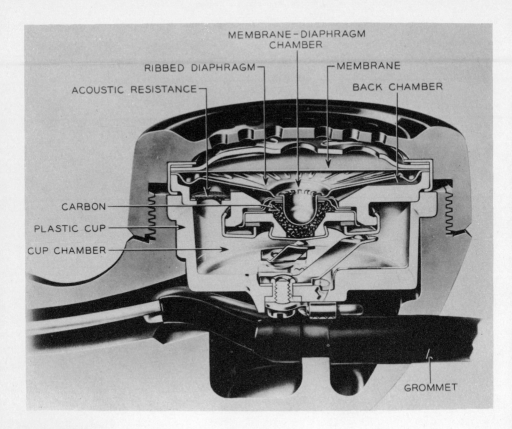

MEMBRANE–DIAPHRAGM
CHAMBER

RIBBED DIAPHRAGM

MEMBRANE

ACOUSTIC RESISTANCE

BACK CHAMBER

CARBON

PLASTIC CUP

CUP CHAMBER

GROMMET

*Actual mechanism of
the transmitter*

# The Telephone's Mechanism

*Actual mechanism of
the receiver*

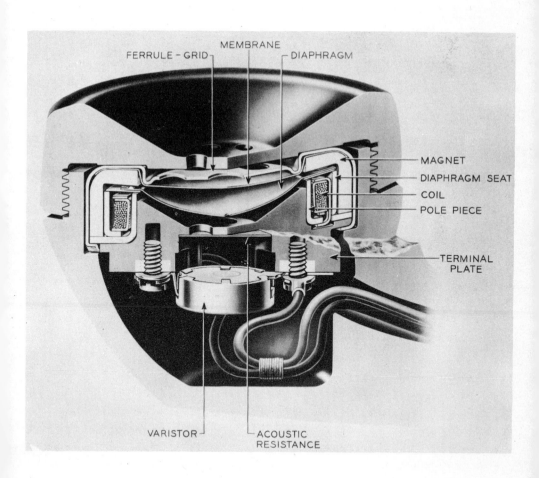

FERRULE – GRID  MEMBRANE  DIAPHRAGM

MAGNET
DIAPHRAGM SEAT
COIL
POLE PIECE

TERMINAL
PLATE

VARISTOR  ACOUSTIC
RESISTANCE

*Inside the main offices of the telephone company on West Street, New York*

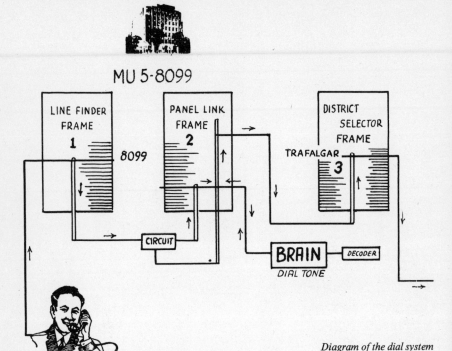

*Diagram of the dial system*

and why only a sketchy outline of its intricate operations can be given here.

The complexity of the problem might be understood more readily if you realize that from a New York City telephone it is possible to dial directly nearly 4,300,000 subscribers in the city and its environs. Soon, through innovations which already have been launched in certain parts of the country, it will be possible for the telephone customer to dial almost any telephone in the United States.

The task of connecting you with the number you are calling falls to several kinds of automatic dialing systems, identified in telephone terminology as Panel, Crossbar, and Step-by-Step. All these systems are interconnecting, so that it is possible to make an out-going call through an office employing one system and to have the call received in an office using another. Although the Crossbar system, which incorporates the latest refinements in telephonic science, is gradually being installed in most telephone buildings, for purposes of discussion we have selected the Panel system because it is visually the simplest.

Suppose you are in midtown Manhattan and you want to dial your home at TR (for TRafalgar) 7–9598. You pick up your office telephone, which is MU (for MUrray Hill) 5–8099, and instantly you are connected with the Murray Hill office, where one of sixty rods on one of twenty-five huge line-finder frames moves up to your particular line (hori-

TR 7-9598

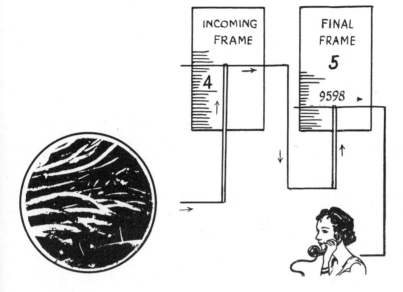

zontal line number 8099). Each sub-scriber has his own particular line. The line-finder frame is represented by 1 in the diagram. There is one of these frames for each 400 sub-scribers.

The panel-link frame (number 2 in the diagram) instantly connects your line finder with a sender, or brain, as it might be called. This brain is a com-plex instrument which controls most of the automatic connecting. As soon as you reach it, you hear the dial tone, and, as you get this tone almost the second you pick up your phone, you can see how fast the connection is made through these two frames.

If the brain could talk, it would say: "I'm ready to take your call and con-nect you with any number you wish";

so you answer by dialing TR 7-9598. In doing this you make seven mo-tions. Each motion makes a number of little clicking sounds behind your dial. The letters $T$ and $R$ are really numbers 8 and 7, so the $T$ gives 8 clicks, the $R$ gives 7 clicks, the next 7 gives 7 clicks, the 9 gives 9 clicks and so on, until you have dialed TR 7-9598. All these clicks are tiny im-pulses which affect scores of little electromagnets in the brain, and which, with the aid of the decoder, lo-cate available outgoing trunk lines on the district-selector frame (number 3 in the diagram).

The district-selector frame carries trunk lines to all the city central of-fices, such as Plaza, Beekman, But-terfield, and so on. The Murray Hill

*Alexander Graham Bell
in 1876*

*Bell's original centennial magneto transmitter*

section, one of the busiest in the city, carries at least 450 trunks on this frame. (A satellite office-selector frame, which can be called into play if necessary, gives access to another 450 trunks, making a total of 900 available for the call.) As the brain receives the coding information from the decoder, it directs the district rod to an available TR 7 trunk and makes the connection. (Meanwhile, the dial tone ceased as soon as you started to dial.)

MU 5–8099 is now connected with the incoming frame at the Trafalgar 7 office. At this point the four numeral digits (9598) will be used by the brain to direct the call on the incoming and final frames to one number out of a possible 10,000 in the Trafalgar 7 office. The incoming frame has five huge banks, each giving access to 2,000 lines located on four final frames,

each serving 500 lines. When the connection is made with the final frame, up goes one of the rods to connect with horizontal line 9598. At this point the brain is notified that its mission is accomplished. The brain then releases itself from the call, and the bell at the called number rings. If the line is busy, the final selector circuit is notified to return a busy tone.

You are thus connected with your home in less than half a minute, without ever realizing the maze of relays, rods, electromagnets, condensers, counters, electric bells, and many other performers that take part in this amazingly complicated operation. Everything works smoothly and perfectly and with split-second timing. While you are talking, thousands of others are doing the same, and the constant clicking of millions of tiny electromagnets and rods moving up and down in the huge labyrinths of wires, relays, and other electrical equipment, is positively amazing!

*The garret, 109 Court St., Boston, where Bell verified the principle of electrical speech transmission*

## 5.  The Vacuum Tube

The vacuum tube, together with the electromagnet, has made radio, television, overseas telephony, radar, the complex electronic computing machines, and hundreds of other twentieth-century inventions possible. It is so much a part of our present civilization that a knowledge of its working principle is essential.

The vacuum tube is made in hundreds of different sizes and shapes, varying from the simple rectifier to the enormously complicated pentode and hexode. Some tubes are glass and others are metal. Some are tiny, no larger than a peanut; others are very large, several feet high. The essential parts of any vacuum tube are a filament of high-resistance wire, which will get very hot and glow when a current is sent into it, and a metal plate near the hot filament. Both, of course, are enclosed in a tube from which the air has been exhausted. In the simplest of all vacuum tubes, known as a rectifier, the metal plate

*The birthplace of the telephone, 109 Court St., Boston. On the top floor of this building, in 1875, Bell carried on his experiments and first succeeded in transmitting speech by electricity*

# ATOMIC STRUCTURE

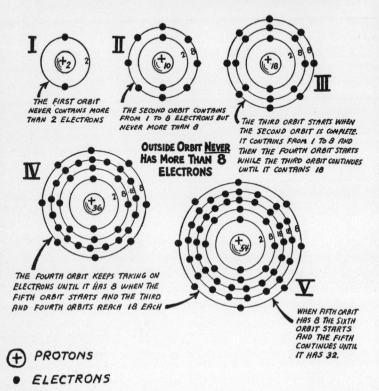

I THE FIRST ORBIT NEVER CONTAINS MORE THAN 2 ELECTRONS

II THE SECOND ORBIT CONTAINS FROM 1 TO 8 ELECTRONS BUT NEVER MORE THAN 8

III THE THIRD ORBIT STARTS WHEN THE SECOND ORBIT IS COMPLETE. IT CONTAINS FROM 1 TO 8 AND THEN THE FOURTH ORBIT STARTS WHILE THE THIRD ORBIT CONTINUES UNTIL IT CONTAINS 18

OUTSIDE ORBIT NEVER HAS MORE THAN 8 ELECTRONS

IV THE FOURTH ORBIT KEEPS TAKING ON ELECTRONS UNTIL IT HAS 8 WHEN THE FIFTH ORBIT STARTS AND THE THIRD AND FOURTH ORBITS REACH 18 EACH

V WHEN FIFTH ORBIT HAS 8 THE SIXTH ORBIT STARTS AND THE FIFTH CONTINUES UNTIL IT HAS 32.

⊕ PROTONS

● ELECTRONS

*Schematic diagrams of the various atoms. Electrons are shown as black dots revolving around the central nucleus in orbits at tremendously high speeds. Hydrogen, the simplest element, has only one proton in its nucleus and only one electron revolving around it. It has no neutrons. Uranium, the most complex natural element, has 92 protons in its nucleus as well as 146 neutrons and 92 electrons revolving around this nucleus.*

is charged with an alternating voltage. In the radio vacuum tubes (and there are many) the metal plate is always positive (+), and a thin wire mesh, known as a grid, is interposed between it and the hot filament.

Since all vacuum tubes are electronic in their action, it is essential before we get acquainted with them to study briefly the structure of the atom and the properties and behavior of the electrons in it.

Atoms are made up of tiny, invisible electrical charges. Small as the atom is (and 10,000,000 will fit comfortably on the head of a pin, with room to spare), it is mostly empty space! Somewhere near the center is the core or nucleus, one trillionth the size of the atom itself! Packed into this nucleus are positive charges called protons, neutral particles called neutrons, and other lesser-known particles that form the mass of the atom. This nucleus is tough and very hard to break up. It is the breaking up of the atom's nucleus, and the extremely complicated theories that developed in the process and from the results, that give us the science of nuclear physics and atomic energy.

Electrons are negative charges that go whizzing around the central nucleus at enormous speeds and in various orbits, somewhat the way the planets in the solar system revolve around the sun. They are called planetary electrons, and, unlike the protons, neutrons, and other particles that are "locked up" inside the nucleus, planetary electrons are *outside* the nucleus and often free to leave the atom. They may be removed by friction, as is the case when a comb is rubbed through one's hair on a cold day, or they may be driven off by heat, as is the case when a red-hot filament glows in a vacuum tube.

*The flow of electrons from one object to another, or from one point to another is the electric current.* The current can be caused by electrons moving along a wire or through a metal, or it may be caused by the flow of electrons through rarefied gas or vacuum. It is the passage or movement of billions of trillions of electrons from a glowing filament (from which they are constantly driven off by the heat) to a positively charged metal plate, that enables us to control current in any way we wish inside of a vacuum tube.

**EDISON "MISSED THE BOAT."** Thomas A. Edison, with more than a thousand valuable patents to his credit, was too

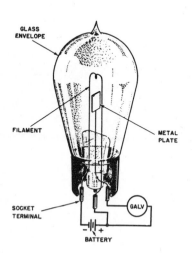

GLASS ENVELOPE

FILAMENT

METAL PLATE

SOCKET TERMINAL

GALV

BATTERY

*The simple Fleming valve, a rectifier tube*

*Thomas Alva Edison
(1847–1931)*

busy inventing the carbon-granule transmitter for the telephone and improving Sholes' typewriter to take advantage of his own discovery. *He had the vacuum tube in the palm of his hand and didn't realize it!* He had already invented the incandescent lamp, in which a filament glows with intense heat under the impact of the electric current. The first lamp was a crude affair in which a carbon filament was used. In one of his experimental bulbs Edison sealed a little plate of copper near, but not touching, the filament.

He sent a charge of positive electricity into the copper plate and was surprised to observe a current of negative charges flowing from the filament to the plate. This was certainly strange, since there was a decided gap between the filament and the plate. Edison thought enough of this phenomenon to patent it in 1883, and it was well known to scientists who followed him as "the Edison Effect."

The Edison Effect lay dormant for about twenty years. In 1899 an accurate and epoch-making explanation

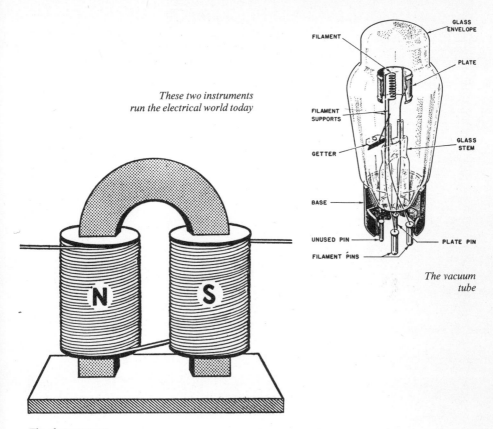

*These two instruments
run the electrical world today*

FILAMENT

GLASS
ENVELOPE

PLATE

FILAMENT
SUPPORTS

GLASS
STEM

GETTER

BASE

UNUSED PIN

PLATE PIN

FILAMENT PINS

*The vacuum
tube*

N    S

*The electromagnet*

of the Edison Effect was advanced by a British scientist, Sir J. J. Thomson. He presented the theory that small, negative particles of electricity, called electrons, were emitted by the filament in Edison's lamp as a result of operating it at incandescence or white heat. He said, further, that these electrons, because of their negative charge, were attracted to the positively charged plate. Thus, as long as the filament was heated to the proper temperature, electrons would flow from it to the plate. This movement

of electrons constituted a flow of electron current, and the electron stream was the means by which the gap was bridged across the intervening space between the filament and the plate, thus closing the circuit.

In 1904 Sir John Fleming, an English physicist, studied this effect and produced a vacuum tube with a smaller and hotter filament and a plate that carried an alternating current, one instant positive and the next instant negative, alternating about sixty times per second. Just as he ex-

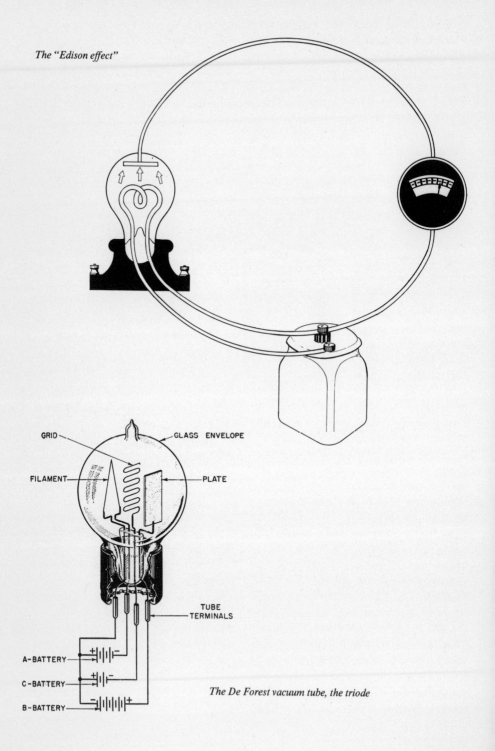

The "Edison effect"

GRID

GLASS ENVELOPE

FILAMENT

PLATE

TUBE
TERMINALS

A-BATTERY

C-BATTERY

B-BATTERY

The De Forest vacuum tube, the triode

pected, when the plate was positive, electrons rushed over to it from the filament. But when it was negative, these electrons were repelled and none reached the plate. The current that emerged from the tube was therefore all in one direction, or direct, instead of alternating. Fleming had transformed alternating current into direct current. This tube, or valve as it is called, is used today and called a rectifier. It is also known as a diode, because it has two and only two essential parts.

**LEE DE FOREST AND THE RADIO VACUUM TUBE.** In 1906 modern radio and television were born with the invention of the triode, or audion, tube. Lee De Forest, an American engineer, was the first to insert a wire grid between the filament and the plate of the Fleming valve. This was one of the most important inventions of the century, for it not only gave us radio and television, but it made possible radar, loud-speaker systems, long distance telephony, sound movies, photographic transmission, the electron microscope, calculating machines, and scores of other electrical inventions. One of the main functions of the De Forest tube is to amplify the tiny, feeble current produced by the radio waves that reach the antennae of our sets. These waves fill all space, but their effects are far too weak and feeble to make any kind of impression on the loud-speaker or television screen. By amplification and multiple amplification in the De Forest tubes, we can bring them to life and make the effects as strong and powerful as we wish. We can amplify any sound to such an extent that the noise made

by a fly walking on a pane of glass would deafen you.

The same thing is true in reverse when we broadcast. The electrical pulsations which come from the microphone in the studio must be amplified many millions of times before they are hurled through space. If they are not, they will never reach their destination.

Radio and television work by changing sound waves and light

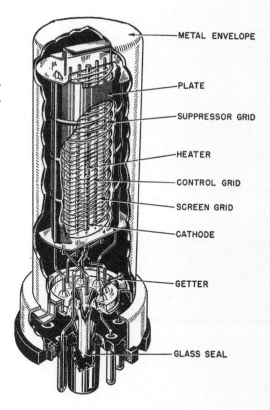

METAL ENVELOPE

PLATE

SUPPRESSOR GRID

HEATER

CONTROL GRID

SCREEN GRID

CATHODE

GETTER

GLASS SEAL

*The complicated pentode tube*

*Replica of Edison's original electric light*

waves into electrical pulsations that are too weak to be used as is. The vacuum tube intensifies or amplifies these pulsations millions of times and sends them out over the ocean or across the continent. By the time they arrive at the other end of their long journey (accomplished in less than a fiftieth of a second), they are again weak and feeble, and the vacuum tubes in your radio and television sets step them up once more to make them strong enough to produce sound in the loud-speaker of the radio or the receiver of your telephone and to light pictures on the screen of your television set.

Many different kinds of vacuum tubes are used for hundreds of different purposes. One type of vacuum tube in particular, working on an entirely different principle, turns light energy into electrical energy. It is known as the photoelectric cell, sometimes called the electric eye. Because the vacuum tube is as sensitive and as instantaneous in its reaction as the electromagnet, it is just as useful, and its part in the drama of modern inventions cannot be overestimated. In in-

*Lee De Forest*

dustry the electric eye (photoelectric cell) performs all kinds of counting, sorting, timing, recording, and similar operations that have been invaluable to industry. In medical therapy the vacuum tube has produced X-ray therapy, high-frequency applications in bloodless surgery, and other vital tools for the medical profession. In scientific research the vacuum tube has produced the electron microscope and the amazing and intricate electrical brains in the computing machines, which can multiply fourteen digits by fourteen digits in a fiftieth of a second and solve in hours mathematical problems that would take an expert mathematician years to solve. In military communications radar is one of the most important inventions to come from the vacuum tube.

It is very difficult to realize that all of these inventions are less than fifty years old. Just as the nineteenth century produced the miracle of the electromagnet and all the marvelous inventions that grew out of it, so the twentieth century produced the miracle of the vacuum tube and all the remarkable inventions just mentioned. The comparatively new transistor, which substitutes for the vacuum tube in many cases, promises to loom large on the future scientific horizon, and the next fifty years should produce more wonderful inventions, undreamed of today.

**THE WORKING PRINCIPLE OF VACUUM TUBES.**    While the theory of electron tubes and the mathematics involved are both difficult and complicated, and a working knowledge of the many kinds of vacuum tubes requires a full college course in electronics, the general principle on which these tubes work is surprisingly simple.

Coulomb's law states that "the force of attraction (or repulsion) between two charges is directly proportional to the product of their charges and inversely proportional to the square of the distance between them." We are concerned here with the distance between these charges. The nearer two charges are to each other, the greater the force will be, so if a positively charged plate were very near a filament which is emitting negative electrons, the effect of that plate on the electrons will be very much greater than it would be if the plate were far away from the filament.

Now look at the diagram on page 191. A direct current of electrons flows smoothly and steadily from filament

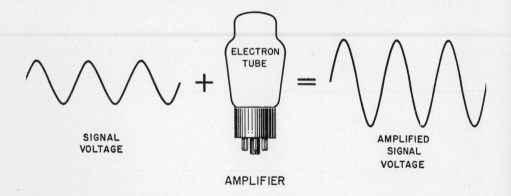

SIGNAL
VOLTAGE

ELECTRON
TUBE

AMPLIFIED
SIGNAL
VOLTAGE

AMPLIFIER

*This shows how the signal voltage is*
*amplified in passing through the electron tube*

*F* to the positively charged plate *P*. As long as the current flows, it will go from the filament to the plate and *never* from the plate to the filament. It is a one-way street, for in the triode and most of the other vacuum tubes the filament is always giving off electrons, and so it always has a cloud of negative charges surrounding it, and the plate is always charged positively. In most of these tubes the filament is *never positive* and the plate is *never negative*.

It is the wire grid which De Forest added that makes the vacuum tube so valuable. This grid is always charged with *alternating* voltage, and so we have: a filament which is always emitting negative charges (electrons), a grid that varies from positive to negative many times per second, and a plate which is always positive.

Since the grid is very much nearer filament *F* than plate *P* is, any charge on the grid will have a much stronger effect on the electrons than an equal charge would if it were on the plate. If the grid is negative, the electrons that are emitted from the filament will be repelled. They will collect and move around in the space between the grid and the filament, and very few will get over to the plate. The very next instant in which the grid becomes positive, a much greater attractive force is set up between it and the filament. This added force, this drawing from the neighborhood of the filament of hundreds of trillions *more* electrons than could be produced without the grid, together with the added electrons that had collected when the grid was negative, rush *through the mesh of the grid*, over to the positively charged plate, which is still pulling electrons to it the way it did before the grid was introduced. You can see, then, that this added force, causing an extra supply of electrons to move over to the plate, greatly increases the current on that plate. In other words, when the grid is positive, there is a decided increase in current to the plate, and when it is negative, there is little or no current at all. The effect of a feeble wave sent into the tube will thus be amplified.

But now we come to a perplexing situation. When the grid is negative and no electrons reach it, what happens to the charge on the plate? We already know that the current leaving this constantly positive plate is direct current. How can this be? How can a perpetually positively charged plate produce "alternating current," and amplified alternating current at that? Now look at the diagram on page 192. The charges on the plate, instead of becoming negative, become less positive. And instead of becoming positive they become more positive. These alternations are in exact accord with the alternating current in the grid and have exactly the same effect as alternating current, even though it is all positive and produces a curve that is always above the zero

axis, instead of a curve that is alternately above and below the zero axis.

So, a current so weak as to be almost nonexistent can be amplified in the De Forest tube. By sending this amplified alternating current into a circuit containing a resistor, then into another vacuum tube, we can amplify it still more, and so with more tubes or tubes of different construction we can amplify and control incoming radio waves in any way we please. When we discuss the radio, we shall see just how the signal current is amplified in the next tube, but here it is only necessary to say that it *is* amplified in that tube.

**THE PHOTOELECTRIC TUBE.** Remarkable in its construction, action, and application is the photoelectric tube, which is different from all the other vacuum tubes. Instead of using electrical energy to produce light, as is the case

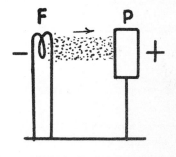

*Electrons flow*
*uninterrupted from filament* F *to plate* P

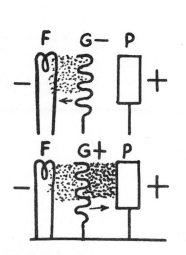

*The grid* G *is introduced. When*
*it is − no electrons get over to plate* P; *when*
*it is + an added force is placed upon* P
*by the onrushing electrons.*

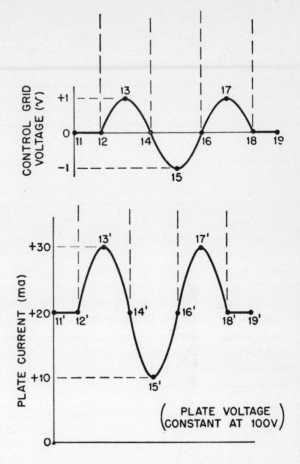

*This shows the plate current is alternating in spite of the fact that it is all above the O axis. Instead of being alternately + and −, it is MORE + and LESS + alternately, and this produces the same effect as alternating current.*

with the electric lamp, the photoelectric tube uses light to produce electrical energy.

These amazing tubes transform fluctuating energy into sound vibrations, to make the movies talk. Millions of tiny dots, working on the same principle, are spread over the camera plate in the television studio in order to produce the electrical picture which entertains you on your television screen. The photoelectric tubes also perform miracles in sorting, counting, color comparing, and timing to ten-thousandth of a second in our industrial machinery, they hurl photographs through space, and they are the basis of the great calculating "brains" in the mechanical solution of mathematical problems that might have baffled the late Dr. Einstein.

The principle on which the photoelectric tube works was discovered in 1887 by Heinrich Hertz, the scientist whose researches in radio waves paved the way for Marconi and De Forest. This great discovery, like many others of equal importance, was made by accident while he was carrying on extensive experiments with electromagnetic waves. Hertz noticed that the spark between the terminals of his detecting circuit passed much more rapidly when there was light on the primary terminals than when there was no light. Hertz concluded that light had a definite effect on the emission of electrons, but the physics of his time prevented him from producing a photoelectric tube.

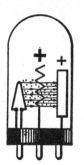

*The vacuum tube*

Further investigations and experiments in the complex structure of light produced one of the fundamental constants in nature, known as Planck's Constant, and paved the way for Einstein, who in 1905 gave the world one of the most important equations or laws in modern physics— the famous photoelectric equation which shows the relation between radiation and electrical energy in terms of light quanta.

From the minds of the giants of science whose only tools are a pencil, a pad of paper, and genius, came the intricate mathematical equations, and out of these equations the modern photoelectric tube was born.

The fact that light has a definite effect on the atoms of matter is shown by the photographic plate. Wherever light strikes the plate, it actually breaks the molecules of the silver-salt emulsion, collecting the silver atoms to form an opaque screen, which is black. In a somewhat similar way the effect of light on the atoms of the rare element cesium sets cesium electrons free. This is a little different from the photographic plate, where molecules were broken up into atoms. Here the atoms themselves are robbed of electrons in exact proportion to the intensity of light that strikes the cesium, provided the light is above a certain minimum frequency.

On the next page we see a vacuum tube with a semicircular piece of thin silver coated with a multiple layer of cesium oxide on top of which is a layer of the rare element cesium itself. The rod in the center is the positive plate. When light strikes this semicircular strip, electrons flow over to the positively charged rod or plate in the center, and thus a current is set up, since the electric current is nothing more than the flow of electrons from one point to another. The semicircular strip, then, acts in the same way as the filament does in the ordinary vacuum tube, and it gives off electrons in exact accordance with the intensity of light which strikes it. The slightest change in light intensity—a change as slight as one fifty-millionth part of the original—will affect the current in the photoelectric tube and

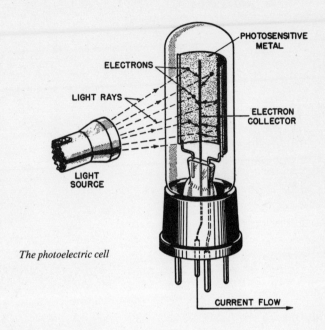

PHOTOSENSITIVE
METAL

ELECTRONS

LIGHT RAYS

ELECTRON
COLLECTOR

LIGHT
SOURCE

*The photoelectric cell*

CURRENT FLOW

consequently can be recorded. No eye can be anywhere near that sensitivity, and that is why the electric eye is so important in industry. Not only that, the photoelectric tube is absolutely instantaneous in its reaction to light changes, and that is one of the many reasons why it ranks with the most important inventions of this century.

## 6.  The Story of Radio and Television

**RADIO.** After reading the description of the telephone, we know that in order to transmit sound electrically we must turn it into electrical impulses, send these impulses along wires to their destination, and finally turn them back into sound by sending them into an electromagnet, which sets a thin metal disc or paper cone vibrating.

In radio we do essentially the same thing, but without wires. The microphone is, in principle, the same as a sensitive telephone transmitter, and the loud-speaker is, in principle, the same as a sensitive telephone receiver. Obviously the main difference between the telephone and the radio is in the transmitting medium. In radio the sound frequency is made to "ride" on extremely high-frequency electromagnetic waves without any wires at all, and in order to understand how this is done we must know something about these waves.

Before proceeding, let us consider what Maxwell and Hertz actually did. It is to them and to them alone that we owe wireless communication.

*Heinrich Rudolph Hertz (1857–1894)*

*James Clerk Maxwell*
*(1831–1879), the father of electronics*

From the electromagnetic theory of James Clerk Maxwell and its practical application by Heinrich Rudolph Hertz, came the wireless telegraphy of Marconi and the development of radio, radar, television, and radiotelephony.

James Clerk Maxwell was born on November 13, 1831, a very lucky date for the world. In his early boyhood he showed no signs of genius, and was nicknamed "Daffy" by his classmates because he was so different from the others. At fifteen he became interested in mathematics, partly because of the indescribable beauty and power of the subject and partly because it came easy to him. This interest grew to such an extent that at the age of twenty-one he was elected a scholar at Trinity College and some years later was appointed the first Professor of Experimental Physics at Cam-

bridge, one of the greatest honors of the day.

Maxwell had been following the researches of Faraday closely and finally took issue with him as to the medium that transmits the lines of force between the opposite poles of a magnet. By rigorous mathematical analysis he showed that electromagnetic action must travel through space in waves and that these waves, which are identical to light waves in their velocity, consist of disturbances that are transverse to the direction in which they are propagated. Maxwell's theory showed, through the medium of mathematics, that electrical action at

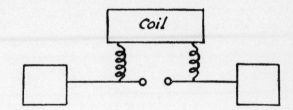

*The Hertz oscillator*

*The Hertz resonator*

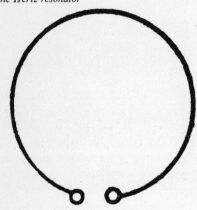

a distance was produced by electrical waves. He predicted that if these waves could be generated, they would travel with the speed of light, and, although nobody had actually produced them to any degree up to that time, he described their properties.

There is a remarkable similarity between the electromagnetic theory of Maxwell in 1873 and the relativity theory of Einstein in 1905. Both theories are revolutionary in their effect on scientific thought. Both theories are incomprehensible to the layman because they are explained in mathematical terms far beyond the ability of most men to grasp. Maxwell, like Ein-

stein, might have said, "Only twelve men in the world will understand what I am saying," and he would have been correct. But concepts as vital and far-reaching as these simply have to be interpreted and applied to actual fact, and just as the relativity theory led to atomic energy, so the electromagnetic theory led to wireless communication. So it remained for another genius to apply Maxwell's theory and put all those complicated equations to practical use. Heinrich Rudolph Hertz was that genius.

Heinrich Rudolph Hertz was born at Hamburg, Germany, on February 22, 1857. During his school days he cherished the ambition to become an engineer, and at the age of twenty he studied at Munich with this profession in view. He soon found that he was more interested in the physical theories on which practical mechanics are based than in the practical details of the subject. Accordingly, in less than a year, he changed his plans, and well it was for science and the world in general that he did so. During the winter of 1877 he read original treatises by the famous physicists of the past, attended lectures on experimental physics, and experimented to the full extent of his time. His studies were thorough and his interest keen, and it is no wonder that when he went to Berlin University in October 1878 he attracted the attention of leading experts and was at once placed on original research work. He won a prize for the best solution of a difficult electrical problem, and became the most notable pupil of Helmholtz, a great teacher and a giant in many branches of science, including mathematics, physics, and chemistry.

One day in 1885 while Hertz was experimenting with some coils of wire and a Leyden jar, he noticed that the discharge of the jar through one of the coils induced an appreciable current in the other coil, provided there was a spark gap in the inducing coil. Hertz, having the curiosity that Oersted had, followed this experiment up with others, and before long he was sending electrical waves across space. His apparatus was extremely simple. It consisted of two parts: the exciter and the resonator.

The exciter was formed by mounting a metal plate at the ends of two metal rods, the other ends of which terminated in metal balls. These balls were separated by a distance of about half an inch. At first the rods were connected to a Leyden jar, but, in later experiments, they were connected to the terminals of the secondary winding of an induction coil. By these means they were charged so that a spark was caused to jump across the gap separating the two balls. The resonator was formed by a wire bent to a circular shape but having a small gap, the ends terminating in two small metal balls. The wire ring was placed a short distance away from the exciter. When the latter was set in action, sparks were seen to jump across the gap in the resonator, although the latter was not connected in any way with the oscillator.

With the exciter to propagate the electric waves and the resonator to detect them at a distance, Hertz reproduced all the phenomena of light, one after another, in corresponding electromagnetic effects, and thus completely demonstrated the identity of light and electricity. He worked with extraordinary skill, both experimentally and mathematically, and quickly perceived that not only could Clerk Maxwell's theory be applied to his discovery, but also that the theory might be elaborated in detail so as to include the whole range of his phenomena. By laborious and difficult experiments he came to know all about his new form of electric waves, publishing his results in a rapid succession of papers addressed to the Berlin Academy of Sciences between November 10, 1887, and December 13, 1889.

Now, what are these waves? Are they the electric current? Are they rapidly moving electrons? Could you light an electric light bulb with them or start a motor going? Just what are they and how do they come to be so important? We know they exist, in spite of the fact that we can't see or hear or feel them. They are everywhere, and yet the only way they can be brought to life is by turning the knob of your receiving set.

If you should get very near the

source of these waves and hold a coil of wire in your hand, a current would be set up in that coil. If the frequency of these electromagnetic waves were high enough, the current in the wire would be strong enough to light an electric lamp or start a motor. But that does not say that these waves are the electric current; they are *not*. They are electromagnetic vibrations in space, which set up an electric current in any good conductor they happen to strike.

We already know that an electromagnet is a piece of iron around which is wound a coil of wire. The electric current flowing through a coil of wire sets up a magnetic field all around the wire. This magnetic field acts upon the molecules in the iron, turning the iron into a magnet. It is the rapid motion of the electrons in the wire that sets up the magnetic field; when the motion of the electrons stops, the magnetic field stops and the iron loses its magnetism. As we have already seen, electricity and magnetism are closely related. When we considered the electric generator, we saw that while current in a coil sets up a magnetic field around the coil, the reverse is also true. Moving a coil of wire in a magnetic field sets up a current in the coil. In either case, *motion* is the important factor.

A wire carrying the regular sixty-cycle alternating house current, which is in general use today, has an electrostatic field (a field of electrons) as well as a magnetic field surrounding it. Because of the low frequency (sixty cycles per second is very low), these two fields hug the wire and do not leave it. As the frequency of the alternating current increases, the two fields gradually start to detach themselves from the wire, and when the frequency reaches half a million or a million alternations per second, the two fields forming an electromagnetic wave leave the wire and travel off in all directions at the speed of light. These, then, are the radio waves, composed of two fields: the electrostatic and magnetic, which are continually varying in phase with each other a half million or more times per second.

The audiofrequency wave, having the frequency of a sound wave (essentially the same wave as was set up in the telephone wires), has a low frequency of anywhere from 100 to 10,000 vibrations per second. We could not send this wave out by itself because this low frequency cannot leave the wire. What we actually do is send it on the high-frequency radio wave, let it travel along on it after being amplified many thousand times by enormous tubes before it leaves the station.

Radio waves penetrate everything except good conductors. As soon as they strike a good electrical conductor (most metals) they start the electrons in the atoms of that conductor in motion, setting up an alternating current in the conductor. The frequency of these waves is determined by the radio station that sends them out. They vary from 500,000 vibrations, or cycles, per second to nearly 2,000,000 cycles per second, and this frequency is always given in kilocycles. A kilocycle is 1,000 cycles, or alternations, per second. If a station works on a frequency of 1,500 kilocycles (1500 on the dial), we know that the frequency of the wave it sends out is 1,500,000 vibrations per second. Various stations have various frequencies. Station WOR, in New York, 710 on the dial, has a frequency of 710 kilocycles, or 710,000 vibrations per second. Other stations have other frequencies, always denoted in kilocycles.

Radio waves are everywhere. They are in your room and out in the street, up in an airplane and traveling along with you in your car. They are all over, hundreds of them, all mixed up together; yet you cannot detect them by any of your five senses. It may interest you to know that right now everything that is metal in your room, or anything else that is a good conductor, including your own body, has a current of electricity passing through it. You can't detect this current, because it is extremely weak and so are the radio waves that produce it. But weak as it is, it is there nevertheless.

The antenna of your radio set, being a good conductor, receives a great many waves of different frequencies, since there are a great many stations broadcasting all at the same time. The current set up in that antenna is therefore extremely complex. All the station frequencies are there, and it only remains to select the one you want. This is done by means of coils of wire and condensers (now called capacitors) which are in every radio set.

Radio waves are often called carrier waves because they "carry" the audio wave along with them. They are constantly radiating from the broadcasting stations, regardless of whether or not the audio wave is with them. They are like a very rapidly moving stairway that keeps on moving up all the time whether there are people on it or not. A radio wave without any audio wave might resemble *a*. It oscillates back and forth from positive to negative a million or more times every second, and it is very

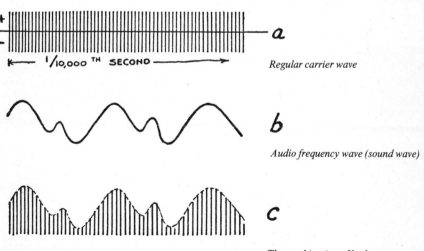

*a*

Regular carrier wave

*b*

Audio frequency wave (sound wave)

*c*

The combination of both waves

steady in its oscillations, as you can see from the diagram.

Now see what happens when an audio wave is sent along on this carrier wave. Illustration *b* shows the very slow wave contour of this audio wave, which is more than a thousand times slower in its oscillation than the carrier, or radio wave. Part *c* shows both waves combined as they leave the transmitter. It must be remembered that the sound, or audio wave, is *electrical* and has no sound at all to it until it enters the loud-speaker.

Let us now consider the capacitor and the coil which form the most important part of every radio receiving set. The capacitor in its simplest form is nothing more than two conductors separated by a nonconductor. That is all there is to it. Two metal plates placed close to each other and separated by glass, or mica, or air, or some other nonconductor of electricity, form a capacitor. A capacitor, which works on the principle of the Leyden jar, stores electric charges somewhat the way a tank stores water. The capacity of a capacitor depends upon two things: the area of the metal plates that are close to, but not touching, each other; and the thickness of the separating nonconductor. The greater the area of the plates and the closer they are to each other (or the thinner the separating nonconductor between them), the greater will be the capacity of the capacitor to hold and discharge electricity. A fine capacitor can be made by taking two pieces of tinfoil, placing them on each side of a piece of waxed paper,

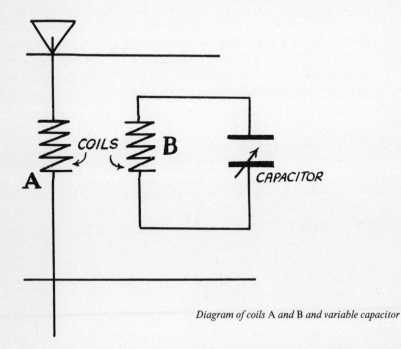

*Diagram of coils* A *and* B *and variable capacitor*

and rolling the whole thing up. The tinfoil is the conductor and the wax paper the insulator, and the sheets of foil are extremely close together.

Now look at the diagram. It shows the antenna extended down through coil *A* and led into the ground. Close to it is another coil, coil *B,* with the same number of turns as coil *A,* in the circuit with a capacitor. The antenna, coil *A,* and the ground form a capacitor which is very weak. The antenna and ground are conductors, and the air between is the insulator. The other capacitor in the circuit with coil *B* is similar to the variable condenser shown on the next page.

Because of the incoming radio waves, the various and extremely complicated magnetic fields in *A* set up the same various magnetic fields in *B.* In the circuit of coil *B* the capacitor and coil work together. And so we have a conglomeration of currents flowing through this circuit and through the capacitor, each current having a particular wave frequency.

Before going further, let us consider the following. Let us suppose that a mechanical source is capable of vi-

brating at various frequencies from 100 to 10,000 per second, and that a nearby tuning fork has only one frequency, namely 450 per second. As the source starts vibrating it sends out air waves which have no effect on the fork until 450 of them per second reach fork *B.* At that point, this second fork starts to vibrate and will continue to do so as long as the frequency is kept around 450. As soon as the frequency gets beyond 450, the second fork stops vibrating. This is called resonance, and it is just what takes place in the capacitor and coil of your set.

Now let's go back to our diagram. If there were no capacitor in the *B* circuit, the very same conglomeration of frequencies would flow through that circuit as flow through coil *A.* But since we have introduced a capacitor into the circuit, we automatically sift out all the frequencies (broadcasting stations) except one particular one. We could take this capacitor out and put in another one which would sift out all the frequencies (broadcasting

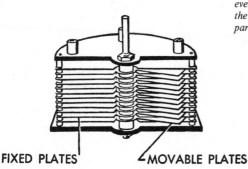

*Variable capacitor (condenser) in every radio set. By turning your dial you vary the capacity of this condenser and select the particular wave frequency or station*

FIXED PLATES        MOVABLE PLATES

stations) except another particular one, and so change the capacitors for each wave frequency. That, of course, would be utter foolishness, so we introduce the *variable* capacitor.

We already know that the capacity of the capacitor depends upon the area of metal that is close to, but not touching, the other metal. If there is a wide area of metal present, the capacity will be great; if there is a small area, the capacity will be small. This capacity to hold and discharge the current varies as you turn the knob of your set. By varying the areas of metal between which is the nonconductor (air in this case), you vary the capacity of the capacitor, and by varying the capacity of the capacitor, you automatically favor one particular current (which is really the wave frequency of the station) in preference to all others.

As you turn your radio knob, you move the movable plates away from or toward the stationary plates. So the total area of metal separated by the thin section of air becomes more or less, and consequently the various currents that enter this capacitor become stronger or weaker, as the capacity of the capacitor to hold them varies. Station WABC might have a frequency that carries a strong current, but if the movable plates are far out and away from the stationary plates in the capacitor, the capacity will be too weak to take on this frequency and favor it above all the others in the circuit. It will then be up to you to turn the knob back so that the correct area of movable plates is close to the stationary plates. As soon as you do this, you will find WABC coming in stronger and stronger.

Once the station you desire is selected from the many others, the tiny, very weak pulsations from it are sent from the aerial directly into the grid of the first vacuum tube and amplified hundreds of times with other tubes, as explained in the beginning of this section, after which they are strong enough to be sent into the electromagnet (whether it be a coil or a magnet) in the loud-speaker. This vibrates a thin piece of metal attached to a paper cone, and the electric audiofrequency wave is turned back into sound in the studio, just the way the telephone receiver does it.

This briefly is the story of how radio works. It is by no means complete, for there are many other electrical devices in your receiving set. There is, for example, the transformer, which turns the house voltage into the required voltage for the set; there is the rectifier, which turns alternating current into direct current; there is the detector, which demodulates the frequency and enables the slower soundwave frequency to emerge without the carrier wave. All these and many more parts make up your receiving set.

TELEVISION. The first television set was designed by G. R. Carey, of Boston, as early as 1875. While it was extremely ingenious and clever, it was highly impractical. It consisted of a regular mosaic of selenium cells, each cell connected by a separate wire to a tiny electric lamp. The cells reacted to light in much the same way that the photoelectric cell does today, and the image was thus transmitted in one lump without motion. No matter how small the tiny electric lamps were on

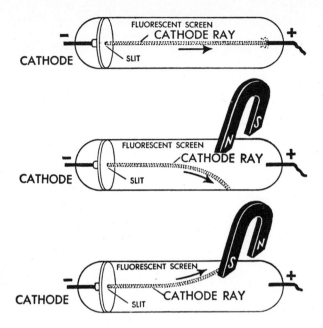

*The effect of a magnet on the cathode beam*

the receiving end, the resulting picture was too crude to distinguish. Furthermore, to produce a clear image by this means would require many millions of electric lamps.

In 1884 Dr. Paul Nipkow, of Berlin, Germany, improved upon Carey's idea by introducing the scanning disc. This was a rapidly rotating metal disc with holes in it, which moved in front of the subject and broke up the light, dividing the picture into sections. Obviously the disc had to rotate at a terrific speed in order to get a reasonably good picture.

The Nipkow system was actually used during the early 1920's. But no matter how much improvement was made on the scanning disc, the rotation was far too slow to produce a satisfactory picture. So the users of television in the twenties had to be content with hazy and blurred pictures which moved like shadows on a crude screen.

In the late twenties and early thirties the great depression stopped investors from putting money into the improving of television, especially when the scanning-disc principle was doomed to sure failure. Just as engineers and businessmen were ready to call television a wild dream, too far off to consider, Dr. Vladimir Kosma Zworykin, a brilliant Russian scientist, started experimenting with the newly discovered cathode beam. Realizing the inconceivable speed at which this beam moves when under the influence of electromagnets, and knowing the importance of almost instantaneous speed in television broadcasting, Zworykin invented the iconoscope, which uses the cathode ray or electron beam to do the scanning. So fast is this amazing beam that the highest-speed scanning disc would seem to be stationary by comparison.

Zworykin obtained a patent on the iconoscope in 1928, and the Radio Corporation of America spent ten years and more than $4,000,000 perfecting it. During this time Philo Farnsworth invented the "dissector" tube for receiving the electrical pulsations and turning them back into pictures. By 1938 both of these tubes were perfected, but their manufacture was stopped by the Second World War and it wasn't until 1946 that the television we know today became a practical reality. To Zworykin and Farnsworth, more than any others, we owe our enjoyment of television. If they hadn't introduced the cathode ray (electron beam) into telecasting and receiving sets there could be no practical television.

**HOW TELEVISION WORKS.** In television a vibrating electrical picture, as it were, is hurled out in all directions from the broadcasting station. How these light vibrations are created, sent out into space, collected, and turned back into their original form is the story of television.

In order to reproduce a photograph in a newspaper or in a magazine, it must be printed from a metal plate. You cannot, however, simply reproduce a photograph directly on the metal plate and etch the metal for printing, because there are all kinds of contrasts of light in the photograph—lights and shadows, black, white, and gray—which the metal plate could not show. In order to reproduce a photograph, the half-tone process is necessary (see the description of this in the Appendix of this book). The picture is taken through a fine wire screen which breaks it up into tiny specks.

If you examine a newspaper photograph through a magnifying glass, you will see these specks very clearly. If the specks are large and close together, a dark area appears; but if they are small and widely separated, a light-gray or whitish area appears. The point to remember is: the picture must be broken up into tiny dots, and the smaller the dots, the more accurate will be the picture.

This principle is the basis of television. The light from the subject to be televised is sent through a lens and focused on a highly sensitive charged screen and enclosed in a vacuum tube known as an image orthicon.

This screen is composed of millions of microscopic silver globules treated with a surface layer of cesium oxide. Each cesium oxide speck is nothing more, in principle, than a microscopic photoelectric cell working in a manner similar to that described in part 5 of this chapter. The entire plate is covered with these globules, which are so small that they are almost invisible. When light falls on one of them, the globule gives off free electrons and in this way acts as a microscopic photoelectric cell. The greater the intensity of light falling on an individual globule, the more electrons it will give off,

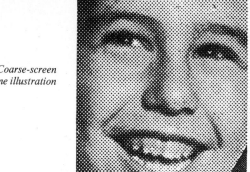

*Coarse-screen*
*newspaper halftone illustration*

*Image orthicon picking up a picture*
*to be transmitted on television*

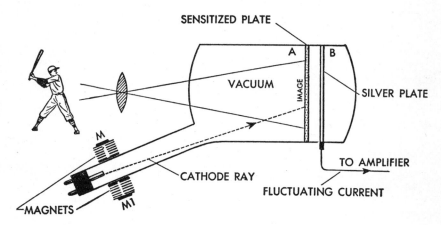

so that a picture focused on the entire plate causes the plate to give off millions of electrons.

Since an electric current is really the flow of electrons from one point to another, millions of tiny negative charges are set up and they flow over to the positively charged plate *B*. In this way they resemble the flow of electrons from the filament to the positive plate in the radio vacuum tube. The plate with the image on it has thus a quantity of minute positive charges induced upon it because of its deficiency in electrons, or negative charges, and these positive charges are distributed over the entire area in exact accordance with gradations of light on the picture which is focused upon the plate. The plate, however, is static; it does not move.

Through a long, narrow cathode tube, a cathode ray is focused. This cathode ray is a bombardment of electrons traveling with terrific speed through a vacuum tube from the cathode to the anode. The stream of electrons is extremely fine and might be compared to a hose playing a stream of water of needle-point thickness on a wall. The cathode beam is now directed at plate *A* and starts to cover it from top to bottom. This is done by regulating two electromagnets, *M* and *M-1*, in such a way that the stream is sent rapidly in one direction and then in the other (cathode rays are influenced by a magnet). The speed of this cathode beam is astonishing. It sweeps across the four-inch plate from left to right in one fifteen-thousandth of a second. Pitched in a slightly downward slope, it sweeps across the odd-numbered lines first, and then goes back and takes in the even numbered lines. It does a complete job of covering each of the 525 lines on the plate thirty times in a single second, and in that time every microscopic speck of cesium-coated silver is covered by the cathode ray. Some idea of the speed of this ray may be had from the following: If you and the cathode ray started to "read" this page, by the time *you* had read a single line, the ray would have "read" 1,200 pages!

The electrons pouring out of the cathode ray in this needle-point stream strike the globules on the plate and fill up the deficiency of each in about a half-millionth of a second. Where the light is intense on the plate, more electrons are required, and where it is not so intense, less electrons are required. The electron stream is like a stream from a hose which is filling up millions of holes

in the earth, each hole having different depths. More water is required for the deeper holes.

The plate is, then, for an extremely small fraction of a second, made electrically neutral, but the change of charge on each particular globule of silver sets up a voltage in the plate, and this voltage is immediately induced into the plain metal plate *B* placed close to it. The second plate *B*, which is merely a piece of metal, usually silver because of its high conductivity, acts as a condenser to the individual globules of silver and stores up these electrical charges exactly the way the original light from the subject produced them. There are thus set up in the metal plate millions of tiny electrical pulsations exactly in accordance with the pulsations or change of voltage in the sensitive plate *A*.

The light coming from the subject which is to be televised is thus first thrown on a sensitive plate which it affects just as light affects a photographic plate. The scanning beam from the cathode ray, or electron gun, as it is called, dissects these tiny differences in sensitivity and makes the whole plate literally vibrate with electrostatic pulsations. These pulsations are then induced onto a metal plate placed close to the sensitive plate and removed from the tube by means of wires.

Obviously the strength of these pulsations is so small that they are absolutely useless, so they must be amplified at least one million times by means of vacuum tubes, before they can be sent to the carrier wave. From the time they leave the broadcasting station in the carrier wave until the

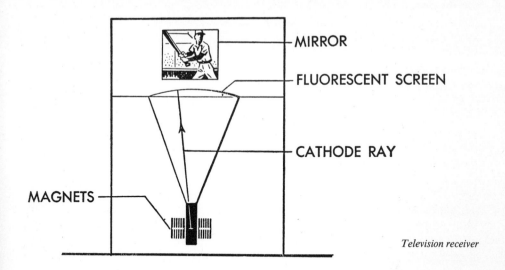

MIRROR

FLUORESCENT SCREEN

CATHODE RAY

MAGNETS

*Television receiver*

time they strike the antenna of your television set, they are exactly the same as radio waves, though their frequencies are different. It now remains to bring them down into your television set and translate them back into light pictures, thereby reconstructing the original scene as televised in the television studio.

In the receiving set we have a long glass vacuum tube in the shape of a megaphone. At one end of this tube is a cathode tube similar to the one in the studio. When the electrical pulsations reach the cathode tube they vary the electron flow. Two sets of magnets control the motion of this cathode ray and cause it to move horizontally and vertically, exactly the way the cathode ray in the studio moved. By focusing this thin stream on a fluorescent screen (a glass screen coated with zinc oxide and other chemicals) and causing it, by means of the vertical and horizontal magnets, to scan this screen in exactly the same way and in exactly the same time as the cathode ray in the studio operated, the picture is reproduced exactly, globule by globule, as it were, on the screen in our receiving set, whose millions of tiny fluorescent molecules vary in intensity in exact accordance with the electron flow from the cathode tube.

It must be remembered that the electron flow from the cathode tube in our receiving set pulsates or varies in current in exact accordance with the way the screen pulsated in the television studio.

Because of the amazing rapidity of the cathode ray and the extreme sensitivity of the electromagnets which guide it, the resulting picture formed on the screen in the television receiving set, in addition to being a perfect reproduction of the scene in the studio, is also a moving picture. The regular speed of a moving-picture projector is between sixteen and twenty-five pictures per second. We have already seen that the number of complete pictures flashed on the screen of the television receiving set is thirty pictures per second. The cathode beam covers the plate in the televising studio in one-thirtieth of a second, and in so doing produces only one complete, stationary picture. Since it produces thirty of these pictures every second and each one varies a trifling amount from the preceding one, the result is perfect continuity of motion.

## 7.  Some Applications of the Electromagnet and the Vacuum Tube

ELECTRICAL SOUND RECORDING. All methods of electrical sound recording and reproduction are essentially the same, regardless of whether wires, movie film, magnetic tape, or radio waves are used.

Sound is nothing more than vibrating air. When air is set into rapid and regular vibrations—so many tiny air waves reaching your ear every second—the result is tone. Two hundred and fifty-six vibrations produce the musical note C; 288 produce the musical note D, etc. When the vibrations are not regular but all mixed up and jangled, the result is noise. It makes no difference whether the sound is tone or noise, it is due to *vibrating air* and nothing else. Without air or some other conducting medium, there could be no sound.

Air vibrations due to sound must be turned into electrical vibrations, which are amplified again and sent into the coils of an electromagnet placed very close to a metal disc in such a way that the varying current, in changing the attractive force of the magnet hundreds of times every second, causes the metal disc to vibrate just as the original sound wave vibrated the air. The whole process may be done in three steps, which are described in greater detail as follows:

1. All sound is vibration in air. It causes the air around it to move to and fro many times per second in the form of waves. This vibrating air strikes a flat thin surface such as the sides of a large empty box or a thin metal disc inside of a ring and produces in them the same vibrations. You can verify this by holding an empty box near the loud-speaker of your radio when it is on full. The sides of the box will actually tickle your hands as they vibrate to the sounds from the loud-speaker.

2. Since these tiny vibrations actually do move to and fro very rapidly, they must in some way be made to vary the strength of an electric current so that the strength and weakness of the current will exactly correspond with the to-and-fro movements of the vibrating medium. This is done in the telephone transmitter and radio microphone. No sound can possibly be recorded electrically without one of these two instruments. The varying electrical vibrations that leave the

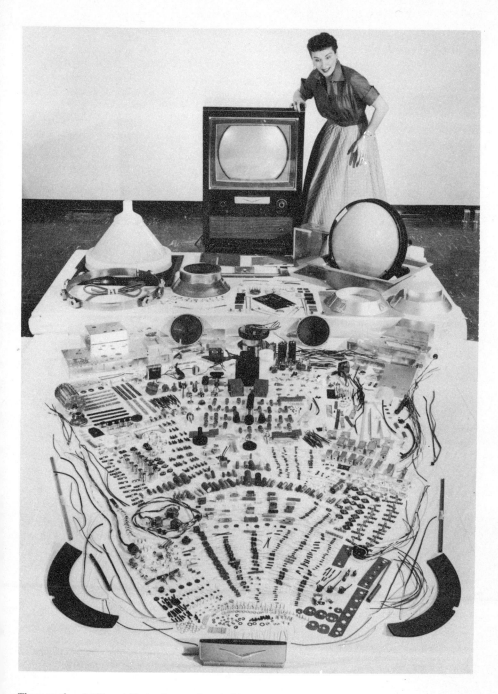

*The more than 1,600 parts that go into a color television receiver*

transmitter or microphone are greatly amplified and sent out in various ways. In the case of the telephone they are sent over wires; in radio they are hurled through space; in sound movies they are made to vary the intensity of an electric lamp and photographed on the side of the film, and in magnetic tape recording they are sent into the coils of an electromagnet, where they induce variations in magnetization on the wire or tape.

**3.** After intensive amplification, these variations in magnetization affect an electromagnet, causing it to vibrate a metal disc placed very close to it, in much the same way that they do in the telephone receiver. The original sound is then reproduced.

**ELECTRICAL TRANSCRIPTIONS.** Since sound is a sensation caused by vibration, its recording must be done by means of vibration, for nothing else can produce sound. In the phonograph record the sound is made to vibrate a thin metal diaphragm which is extremely sensitive to vibrations. This diaphragm is attached by a delicate mechanism to a needle. The slightest vibration of the diaphragm is immediately transferred to the needle, which scratches it onto a moving wax surface. The scratchings on this waxed surface are a record of the sound that made the disc vibrate; it is a visible record when magnified, since it consists of thousands of tiny zigzags or wavy impressions and scratches in the wax. The wax is coated by means of an electrotype process, and a copper electrotype is made. This electrotype is known as the matrix and is used to press out hundreds of records. The records are made of a composition

material which is soft when heated and which is sensitive to the slightest impression when it is subjected to a force of several tons from the matrix. Every scratch and wavy line, no matter how small or insignificant, is faithfully reproduced. When the record hardens, it is an exact reproduction of the original recording.

When the finished record is rotated under a needle attached to a metal diaphragm similar to the recording device, the needle follows in the same tracks which the recording needle made when the sound was recorded. In following these tracks the reproducing needle vibrates the diaphragm of the sound box in exactly the same manner that the diaphragm of the recording apparatus vibrated when the sound was sent into it. Inevitably, then, the sound which comes out of the sound box is an exact reproduction of the sound which went into the recording apparatus.

All sound recording today is done electrically. The old Victrola of forty years ago has long since been supplanted by the electric phonograph. Because of the incredible accuracy and faithfulness of the electromagnet in recording and reproducing sound, the records made by electrical transcription are far better than the records that were made directly from sound vibrations, which we just described.

We already know that current flowing in a coil of wire sets up a magnetic field inside the coil so that any piece of soft iron in that area immediately becomes a magnet when the current is on. We also know from the motor rule that the polarity of the mag-

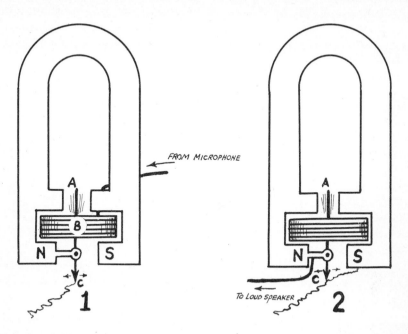

1

To LOUD SPEAKER

2

*To understand these two diagrams better refer to part 4 of the full-page illustration on page 142 showing how mechanical energy is transformed into electrical energy and vice versa. Electrical pulsations from the microphone enter B and cause the bar A to move back and forth and scratch the zigzag groove on a record*

*The point C of the bar A is made to move in the zigzag track thus producing mechanical motion in a magnetic field (the magnet). This motion inside of the coil B sets up the same electric pulsations as came from the microphone and these produce the exact sounds when sent into a loudspeaker*

netized iron inside of that coil of wire changes with the directional change of the current. This is to say, if alternating current, varying in direction many times per second, is sent into a coil of wire, the polarity of the piece of iron will change that number of times per second. Let us assume, for example, that at a given instant the current in the coil flows clockwise, and the top of the piece of iron inside the coil has a north pole of magnetism. The next instant the current will flow counterclockwise, and the top of that piece of iron will change to a south pole of magnetism. Now examine the illustration. It shows a thin iron bar (*A*) supporting a coil of wire (*B*) and pivoted between the poles of a large powerful horseshoe magnet. Alternating current from the microphone, which has already transformed the original sound into the electrical pulsations we have been discussing, enters the coil *B* and continually causes the thin iron bar *A* to alternate in polarity. First the point *C* is north and then it is south, then it is north and then south, and so on, many times per second. But this magnetic bar is pivoted between the poles of a permanent magnet; consequently, because its poles are constantly changing with respect to the poles of the magnet, it will vibrate to and fro very rapidly and the width of its zigzag motion will depend upon the varying current that enters it from the microphone. This bar, which tapers off to a fine needle point, scratches these tiny microscopic zigzags on the soft flat wax, and a metal matrix is made. From this matrix thousands of records are pressed.

In reproducing the sound electrically in the radio phonograph, everything is in reverse order from the recording device. The drawing shows the movable coil between the poles of a powerful magnet, but here the needle, running over the zigzag grooves that the recording needle made, moves back and forth inside the electrified coil and disturbs the magnetic field set up inside it. This causes a pulsating current which moves the needle, and the variations of this pulsating current are identical to those of the current that entered the coils in the recording apparatus. In the first case, electrical energy in the coil produced the mechanical motion of the needle; in the second case, the mechanical motion of the needle produced electrical energy. When the pulsating current is sent into the loudspeaker, it acts upon the electromagnet there in the same manner in which

the original sound acted upon the microphone when the record was made. The result is a perfect reproduction of the sound.

**MAGNETIC TAPE RECORDING.** The magnetic tape seems to upset our ideas of what magnetism is and go contrary to our intuition. If a bar magnet is broken into little pieces, each piece will be an independent magnet with its north and south poles. And if all these pieces are stuck together again, the result will be a single magnet.

It was Valdemar Poulsen, often called "the Danish Edison," who in 1900 discovered that a steel tape can be magnetized in spots, without the magnetism spreading. He reasoned that, since the cores of electromagnets are soft iron, perhaps hard steel would react differently to magnetization. Maybe, if the steel were hard enough, it would be possible to magnetize it in just one tiny spot and leave the rest unaffected. He tried this, and it worked. This set Poulsen thinking. "Maybe," he thought, "it would be possible to magnetize a steel wire or tape to different degrees, according to the varying intensity of an electromagnet, and to have these spots so close together that if the wire or tape were drawn quickly past another electromagnet, these variations would set up a tiny current in the coils of that magnet. This current could then be transferred into sound, just the way it is in the telephone receiver." The theory was perfectly correct, but since in those days there was no such thing as a vacuum tube to amplify the current, there was no way of making it practical.

He built a machine to record sound

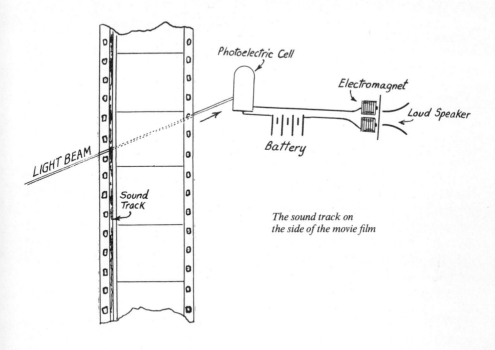

Photoelectric Cell

Electromagnet

Loud Speaker

LIGHT BEAM

Sound
Track

Battery

*The sound track on
the side of the movie film*

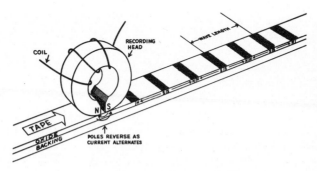

COIL

RECORDING
HEAD

WAVE LENGTH

TAPE

OXIDE
BACKING

N S

POLES REVERSE AS
CURRENT ALTERNATES

*The variations of magnetic intensity on
the tape set up varying electrical pulsations in
the coil which are sent to the loudspeaker*

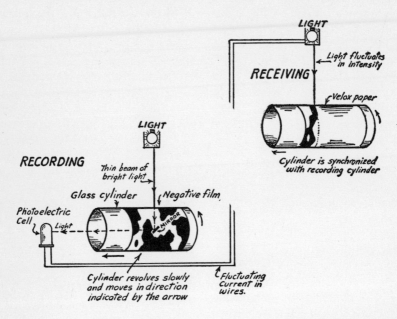

*The recording and receiving of
pictures over the telephone or radio*

on wire or tape and called it the telegraphone. Although the sound from the telegraphone was so weak as to be almost inaudible, the machine *did* work. So Valdemar Poulsen was the first man to record sound on wire and tape, but he never lived to see how far-reaching his amazing invention was.

As a boy, Poulsen was not a good student, but he was intensely interested in physics and drawing. He cared little for mathematics and spent most of his time experimenting. He entered medical school in 1893 at the age of twenty-four but couldn't make the grade, and two years later he got a job in the technical department of the Copenhagen Telephone Company. Here he had plenty of time to explore the mysteries of the telephone, which was still in its infancy. He understood the transmission of sound thoroughly and made many experiments. It was while he was tinkering with a homemade receiver that the idea of magnetic recording came to him. This was such a radically new idea that his telegraphone was exhibited at the Paris Exposition in 1900, and he received honorable recognition.

Magnetic wire and tape recording had to wait for the vacuum tube to make it practical, and even then it was seldom used at first. Records were made by a vibrating needle on soft wax, without the use of the electric current, and these served their purpose very well. And then came the Second World War and Hitler's reign of terror. The Nazis were the first to see the great possibilities in tape recording, and they made use of it. Shortly after the war the Bell Laboratories in New York started doing extensive research on their own, with the result that today practically all sound recording is done on wire or tape.

While the theory of wire and tape recording is involved and can be understood only by electrical engineers and students, the basic principle is extremely simple. The magnetic tape is a comparatively recent invention, now used almost exclusively for sound recording. It is remarkably accurate, records without scratching, plays back readily, and can be erased quickly and easily and used over and over again hundreds of times. Studio recordings are made with a minimum of trouble and worry. If there are any errors, they can be instantly erased and the tape patched like a movie film, so that in the playback these errors will be eliminated. Magnetic tape recorders are used in practically all radio and recording studios. They are used also in schools and colleges and in the home. Many business houses equip their salesmen with these machines, in conjunction with a small movie projector.

Signal currents from a microphone are sent on a very high-frequency al-ternating current through a few vacuum tubes and greatly amplified. They then pass through the coils of an electromagnet, and their varying strength causes corresponding variations in the magnetic strength of the electromagnet. This is precisely what takes place inside a telephone receiver without the metal disc. These fluctuating magnetic impulses affect a plastic tape coated with a magnetic oxide, which is drawn very close to, but does not touch, the magnet. The gap between the poles of the magnet is about .0005 inches. These magnetic impulses are thus induced onto the tape and are somewhat like the photographic sound track on the edge of a movie film. The tape travels along at fifteen inches per second, and when it is made to pass very close to the poles of a similar magnet, the varying magnetic impulses generate a corresponding varying current in the coils of the electromagnet. This is amplified by vacuum tubes and sent into a loudspeaker.

**SOUND FOR MOVING PICTURES.** In producing sound in moving pictures, a microphone is connected in a circuit with an illuminated gaseous tube, and the tiny pulsations in the current coming from the microphone cause the light from the tube to vary in intensity ever so slightly. Any sound that strikes the microphone varies the electric current passing through it. The hundreds of tiny variations in the intensity of the light from the gaseous tube are photographed onto the side of the movie film as the picture is being taken. This is known as the sound track. It is a thin strip which varies in lights and shades many times per second, and the variations are often so delicate and faint that the eye cannot possibly detect any difference in them, but the amazingly sensitive photoelectric cell can and does.

When the film is projected in the movie house, this sound track moves very rapidly between a small, powerful beam of light and a photoelectric cell connected into a circuit with a loud-speaker. As the beam of light passes through the varying shades of the sound track and is focused on the sensitive photoelectric cell, the cell sends into the loud-speaker a reproduction of the current produced by the movie-studio microphone. In other words, the variations in current which enter the amplified loud-speaker in the movie house are the same as the variations in current that came from the studio microphone when it recorded the sounds there. As the loud-speaker operates on the same principle as a greatly amplified telephone receiver or radio loud-speaker, all the electrical pulsations that enter it affect the electromagnet, causing it to attract the paper cone or metal disc and to vibrate it in exact accordance with the way the studio microphone vibrated to the original sound. Since the moving pictures and the sound track run side by side and are perfectly synchronized, the result is a sound movie.

**PICTURES THAT ARE SENT THROUGH SPACE.** The photoelectric cell also plays a vital role in the transmission of photographs and drawings by wire or radio. A photograph of the scene is taken by the cameraman on the spot and immediately developed. The negative, which is a large film, is wrapped around a glass cylinder inside which is a mirror set at a forty-five-degree angle to the axis. Any light that strikes it will therefore be sent out parallel to the axis of the cylinder. This horizontal beam of light is focused on a photoelectric cell which is connected with the telephone circuit or with an apparatus for broadcasting. A very fine, thin, powerful beam of light from the outside passes through the glass cylinder, is focused on the mirror inside the glass cylinder, and is consequently sent directly over to the photoelectric cell by the mirror. Now see what happens when a photographic negative is wrapped around the cylinder: As the cylinder slowly rotates, the beam of light varies in intensity after it has passed through the negative. When the negative is very dark, the beam that strikes the mirror will be very weak, and when the negative is transparent, the beam will pass through it and be very bright when it strikes the mirror. These variations in light intensity are sent over to the photoelectric cell, which faithfully records them in exactly the same manner that it records the sound track on the side of a movie film. The cylinder moves very slowly from right to left while it is rotating, so that in due time every minute portion of the negative has been penetrated by the beam, and every variation in lights and darks on the negative has been recorded by the photoelectric cell and sent, by means of electrical pulsations, to the telephone wires or the broadcasting station.

The receiving apparatus in the news office is the exact reverse of the send-

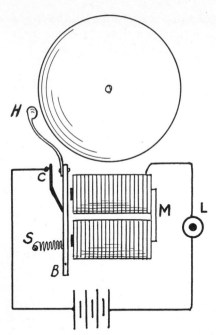

*The electric bell*

sation by means of a microphone (in the case of sound) or a photoelectric cell (in the case of pictures). Send these electric pulsations through space by wire or radio, catch them at the receiving end, amplify them many millions of times, and send them into an electromagnet for sound reproduction, or an electric gaseous tube for picture reproduction. In any case, you can see that these two great performers, the electromagnet and the photoelectric cell, play the vital roles.

**THE ELECTRIC BELL.** Here is one of the simplest and most common applications of the electromagnet. The drawing shows electromagnet *M*, close to which is bar *B*, free to move back and forth about point *P*. This bar has a little extension on it which comes in contact with the circuit closer at *C*. Note that the extension on bar *B* contacts *C* and that there is no gap between *C* and the extension bar. Now see what happens when you press button *L*, completing the circuit and sending current into the magnet. As soon as *M* becomes a magnet it attracts bar *B* to it and causes hammer *H* to hit the gong. But as soon as bar *B* moves over to the magnet, the extension on *B* is no longer in contact with *C*, and the circuit at *C* is broken. *M* is then no longer a magnet. This being the case, bar *B* is no longer held by *M*, and spring *S* pulls it back to make the contact at *C* and close the circuit again. Magnet *M* becomes a magnet again and attracts bar *B*,

ing apparatus. A second glass cylinder with Velox or other sensitized paper wrapped around it moves under a thin beam of light. The cylinder rotates and moves from right to left exactly the way the cylinder in the sending apparatus rotated. Since the source of this thin beam of light is connected in the same circuit in which the variations in current are set up, all the variations in the electric current affect the light and vary its intensity. A positive picture from the negative is thus produced on the Velox in the newspaper office.

It makes no difference whether it is sound or pictures that are sent "hurling through space," the fundamental principle is the same. Change the sound or pictures into electrical pul-

causing $H$ to hit the gong again and disconnecting the circuit at $C$. This allows the bar to be pulled back to $C$ by the spring $S$. You can see that, as long as you keep your finger on button $L$, there will be a continual back-and-forth movement of bar $B$, and hammer $H$ will hit the gong many times per second. As soon as you release the button, there will be no current in the circuit and the bar will move back to $C$ and stay there, since there will be no electromagnet to attract it.

# CHAPTER VII

# WHAT DOES THE FUTURE HOLD FOR US?

Man's transition from one age to the next gains in speed as he becomes more civilized. It took hundreds of thousands of years for prehistoric man to pass from the Stone Age to the Bronze Age, and thousands more to discover the use of iron. But as he acquired more knowledge and was able to unravel and use the secrets of nature to make his life easier, these periods of transition accelerated so rapidly that within the last two centuries he has successfully harnessed steam, gasoline, and electricity to his increasingly complicated machinery, and produced a push-button civilization.

While it is difficult to realize the enormous changes that have taken place in the last century, it is even more difficult to comprehend the changes in the last forty years. Forty years ago there were no such things as radio, high-speed air travel, and television. Parkways were unknown; hand-cranked automobiles chugged and coughed at a top speed of thirty miles per hour along dusty country roads, and the Lackawanna Railroad advertised the use of hard coal for the first time. The movies were colorless and soundless and for the most part streaky and flickery. In medicine, pneumonia, influenza, and tuberculosis were nearly always fatal, because the "miracle" drugs were undiscovered, and most nervous disorders were considered incurable, since psychoanalysis and shock treatments were unheard of. Men and women worked ten and twelve hours a day, six days a week, in sweatshops under conditions which we would consider intolerable today, and the old disease-ridden, rat-infested dumbbell tenements made up the main part of New York's Lower East Side. Bearing all this in mind, you can see what enormous changes have taken place for the betterment of humanity. So it is only natural to speculate on the changes that you will see in your lifetime, changes that are beginning right now.

The past decade will go down in history as the one which ushered in a brand-new age—the Atomic Age. One might say it was born at Alamogordo, New Mexico, on the night of July 16, 1945, for on that night the first atom bomb in history was exploded, sending its enormous mushroomlike cloud of highly poisonous radioactivity miles into the air and turning the night into day for five seconds. The hundred-foot steel tower on which the bomb had been placed was not merely melted by the two-million-degree heat; it was thoroughly vaporized. Nothing, not a trace, was left of it! A man-made sun had actually burst over the New Mexico desert, lighting the country for miles around, and matter was changed to energy by man for the first time. Physicists calculated the force of the bomb to be equivalent to 20,000 tons of TNT, a force which, the following August, reduced the entire city of Hiroshima, Japan, to rubble. Man had at last succeeded in releasing a very small amount of the vast energy locked up inside the nucleus of the atom, an accomplishment which presented him with the choice of blasting civilization to smithereens or using this unlimited new force for his own good.

But the age of the atom did not burst upon the world quite as suddenly as one might think. It started back in 1905 when Albert Einstein, in his theory of relativity, showed mathematically that matter was nothing more than "frozen" energy, and the energy locked up in one pound of matter was enough to send a great ocean liner like the "Queen Mary" around the world. Einstein's simple equation, now famous, was the starting point for all the research and investigation that made the splitting of the atom's nucleus possible.

The revolutionary concept of the equivalence of mass and energy, coming from such an internationally famous scientist whose theory of relativity had already been verified by a total eclipse of the sun, started the world's foremost scientists working on ways and means of splitting the atom, a seemingly impossible task at that time.

The 1920's were an era of great scientific discoveries. In England, Ernest Rutherford, the brilliant physicist, in making a thorough investigation of the emanations from radium and thorium known as alpha particles, was able to calculate the mass of the atom's tiny nucleus, which was already known to consist primarily of positive charges called protons. Following Rutherford came James Chadwick, another British scientist, who used these alpha particles as probes in a now historic experiment with radium and beryllium. A tiny lump of radium in a sphere made of beryllium produced a condition never before seen. The rays from the radium knocked uncharged and neutral particles out of the beryllium atoms and proved to Chadwick that the atom's nucleus was composed of other things besides protons. Chadwick called these newly discovered particles neutrons, because they had almost the same mass as the proton but no charge whatever. Little did he realize that day in 1932 how vitally important these neutrons would prove to be, not only in winning the most terrible war in history but in introducing the world to the Atomic Age.

Shortly after Chadwick's discovery, Enrico Fermi, an Italian physicist in the University of Rome, believed that it might be possible to bombard different elements with these neutrons and, in that way, penetrate the nucleus of the atom to such a degree that the element itself could be changed. This was a modernized idea of the old alchemists, who were always looking for a way to turn silver into gold.

Fermi performed innumerable experiments with one substance after another, exposing each in turn to the steady stream of neutrons pouring from the radium-beryllium source. In many instances new atoms were created that were highly radioactive and did not last too long, but in general Fermi's experiments did not provide the world with anything exceptionally startling. Then he decided to bombard the heaviest element in nature, the one with the greatest number of protons and neutrons in its nucleus, in an effort to make a few more outside neutrons "stick" and produce an entirely new man-made element with unusual properties. Uranium, of course, was the element he bombarded. It is the ninety-second element, and it surely seemed reasonable to assume the addition of more neutrons would produce a still heavier and more complex atom.

The bombardment of uranium by neutrons produced four different and distinct radioactivities, which were mistaken for new elements. Scientists in every country repeated Fermi's experiment again and again in their effort to produce elements 93, 94, and possibly 95. Three of these scientists were Otto Hahn, Lise Meitner, and F. Strassman, who labored for months in their laboratory in Germany for the purpose of isolating new elements. It was through their experiments that a world-shaking event took place. After their bombardment of uranium, two known elements were produced: barium and krypton. This was a complete surprise and disappointment. When you are looking for a glamorous new element and go to so much trouble to make it, you certainly don't want to see old elements appear. Hahn and Strassman repeated the experiment many times, always getting barium and krypton and always being disappointed, until it dawned on Lise Meitner that the uranium nucleus had actually been split. Uranium has ninety-two protons in its nucleus, barium has fifty-six, and krypton thirty-six. If you add barium and krypton together, the protons equal those of uranium. So the uranium nucleus was split for the first time in history, and nuclear fission became an actual fact.

The news that the atom had been split spread like wildfire all over the world, and scientists began analyzing the results of the Hahn-Strassman experiment. With special instruments and accurate calculations, physicists showed that the barium and krypton neutrons did *not* add up to the original uranium neutrons. An appreciable number of the neutrons had been transformed from mass to energy and had been dissipated in the form of radioactive emanations. The uranium atom was likened to an amoeba, the microscopic one-celled animal which reproduces itself by dividing in half. Neutron bombardment divided the complex atom, and this process of division is called fission—nuclear fission.

The Hahn-Strassman experiment was repeated at Columbia University by Fermi, Dr. Niels Bohr, and others, with excellent results. It was then established that nuclear fission could be either controlled or uncontrolled. By controlling it vast quantities of heat could be developed over a long period of time, thus saving millions of tons of coal and oil and giving the world an atomic fuel for the first time. If uncontrolled, a chain reaction could be built up in which the neutrons in the atoms would be set free to bombard other atoms, and the entire mass of uranium could be made to dissipate itself in a catastrophic burst of energy that could destroy an entire city. It was also clear that pure uranium 238 was not the element to produce fission in any large amount; the fissionable part was due to the isotope of uranium—the same element, with three less neutrons in the nucleus. Uranium 235, which is found in extremely small amounts in uranium 238, had to be sorted out and purified before energy could be obtained from matter, and this was a colossal job.

Uranium 235 is the only natural element capable of nuclear fission, and the long-drawn-out and exceedingly complicated process of producing this isotope was well worth the effort and expense in the light of the ultimate results. The search for U-235 was greatly stimulated by the war

that Hitler was about to unleash upon Europe.

On August 2, 1939, Albert Einstein wrote to President Roosevelt, outlining the need for government interest in uranium. The President answered this request by setting up a budget of $2,000,000,000 solely for the purpose of developing atomic energy, and the bomb was made, as everyone knows.

The destructive force of the atom bomb which was dropped on Hiroshima on August 6, 1945, brought World War II to a hasty end, but the peace was not all that it should have been. In the years that followed, a "cold war" between this country and Russia resulted in an atom bomb race which eventually produced the hydrogen bomb. The hydrogen bomb is, by all odds, the most horrible and ghastly weapon that has ever threatened the total destruction of man. Realizing that in another war this H-bomb might be released, the nations of the world turned their attention to the peaceful use of atomic energy and, as everyone knows, a month after the famous "summit meeting" of the Big Four in July 1955, the International Conference of the Peaceful Use of Atomic Energy convened at Geneva, from August 8 to August 20. Here world-renowned scientists discussed ways and means of using atomic energy for the good of mankind.

Before we discuss its peaceful uses, let us try to understand what atomic energy is and why it is so vital to all of us.

The now famous equation of Einstein, $E = Mc^2$, says that the energy locked up in any matter equals its mass times the square of the velocity of light in centimeters per second. This turns out to be $10^{20}$ ergs per gram and there are $13.56 \times 10^6$ ergs to a foot-pound. In the atom of uranium the energy equivalent is .4 erg per atom and since there are about $10^{24}$ atoms in a gram, this energy comes to about $3 \times 10^{16}$ foot-pounds. This figure is far beyond our comprehension and shows that the energy released in the most destructive atom bomb made today is only a small fraction of the total energy inside the atom.

But how do we release this enormous energy? Atoms are so small that 700,-000 of them, piled one on top of the other, would only equal the thickness of this page. All of the atom's energy lies in its nucleus which is one trillionth the size of the atom! No device made by man could ever be small enough to penetrate the atom's tiny nucleus; it can only be done by the particles inside the nucleus, the neutrons. These neutrons must be shot at speeds up to 60,000 miles per second to acquire the great energy necessary to crack the tough nucleus. This speed is about 120,000 times faster than the average bullet. In the laboratory this speed is attained by means of the cyclotron.

The cyclotron is an instrument for giving nuclear particles enormous speeds and, consequently, great energy for the purpose of bombarding the nuclei of certain atoms. Invented in 1931 by Lawrence and Livingston, it consists of two huge metal halves in the shape of the letter D and called D's, placed inside of a vacuum chamber between the poles of a very strong and powerful electromagnet. The two D's are connected to a generator in

*Cyclotron, often called the atom-splitter*

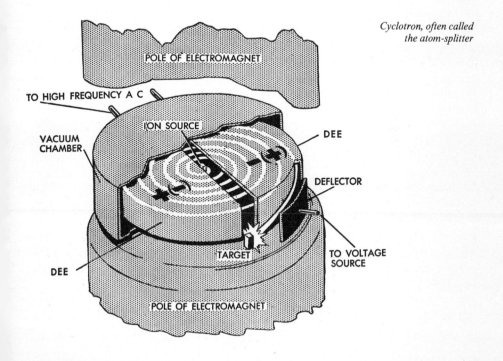

such a manner that their charge alternates between positive and negative millions of times per second. Ionized particles are set free in the center of the cyclotron and are made to travel in a spiral path until they emerge from the rim and are shot plunk up against the element whose atoms are to be bombarded. The particles start between the D's and are guided in their path by a strong magnet. Each time they jump across the gap separating the two D's the polarity of the D's changes and the charged particle is given an additional "kick" which makes it go faster and faster. As its speed increases its mass also increases by the relativity law and by the time these nuclear particles emerge they are traveling at enormous speed, have considerable mass and an amazing amount of energy. A stream of such particles focused on the atoms of certain elements is capable of splitting their nuclei.

In the case of uranium and other fissionable elements, the neutrons are constantly being hurled off by the atoms themselves with such high speed that they actually penetrate other nuclei; these liberated neutrons shoot off with speed and energy enough to penetrate still other nuclei and so on, from atom to atom, forming a chain reaction. This chain reaction takes place inside of some of the radioactive elements, particularly uranium 235, which is an isotope of uranium 238.

Chain reaction is either controlled or uncontrolled. If it is uncontrolled and let "run wild" we have the instant release of part of the energy of each of the $10^{24}$ atoms in a gram, all going off at once and generating heat up to three or four million degrees Fahrenheit. In controlled reaction we slow down the fast neutrons with moderators like cadmium and carbon and allow only one neutron in each three that are released to carry on and keep the chain reaction going. The diagram opposite shows this. For controlled chain reaction we see a neutron n striking an atom of U-235 and causing three neutrons to shoot off. One of these will dissipate into fission waste, another will be absorbed by the atom of U-238 which is always present where U-235 exists, and the third neutron will pass through a moderator like carbon and be slowed down as it enters the next atom of U-235. Here it does the same thing again and the third which was set free from this new atom passes through the moderator and is slowed down when it hits the next atom. This keeps on and on in a thoroughly controlled pace, generating heat as it does so. In this manner we get the same energy that we get out of the atom bomb, only it is distributed over a period of twenty or thirty years instead of a split second. It is slow and steady and generates enough heat to turn water to usable steam instead of being over in a flash and generating a heat of several million degrees.

This controlled chain reaction, called an atom pile, is accomplished by means of a nuclear reactor, of which there are many in experimental use at the present time. The nuclear reactor is really a furnace generating heat by nuclear fission instead of burning coal. In the coal furnace the atoms of carbon combine with the atoms of oxygen in the air to form carbon dioxide gas. Here heat is generated, but the atoms are

## CHAIN REACTION

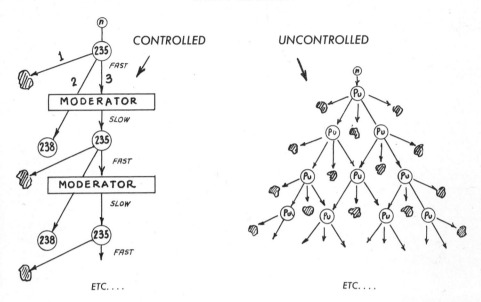

CONTROLLED          UNCONTROLLED

ETC. . . .                    ETC. . . .

not split. They remain intact through-out the process of combustion. In the nuclear reactor the nuclei of the atoms are actually split open and the enor-mous energy inside of them is partly released in the form of heat. The heat thus generated is carried away to form steam which, in turn, is used to run an electric generator.

The diagram at the top of page 226 shows the simplest form of nuclear re-actor. The bars of uranium 238 and 235 are in the proportion of 140 to 1. They are placed inside a well-protected cement enclosure which is filled with heavy water. Heavy water, $D_2O$, is water made from deuterium (heavy hydrogen); and heavy hydrogen, un-like regular hydrogen, has a single neu-tron in its nucleus. (Hydrogen is the only element without any neutrons in

its nucleus.) It is this single neutron that helps heat the water as it circu-lates in and out between the bars of uranium. This water becomes so hot that it can give constant heat to the gas in the heat exchange and this gas is used to heat water and produce steam.

Another type of nuclear reactor is shown at the bottom of page 226. Here an atom pile is inside a very thick wall of concrete which keeps the dangerous gamma rays from escaping. Inside the pile we have two moderators, graphite and cadmium. Both of these absorb fast neutrons and keep the pile from getting out of control. Note the gas (helium) circulating through the pile. It enters at the bottom as cool gas and emerges at the top at a temperature equal to hot flame. It is then led into the cooler where it heats the pipes and

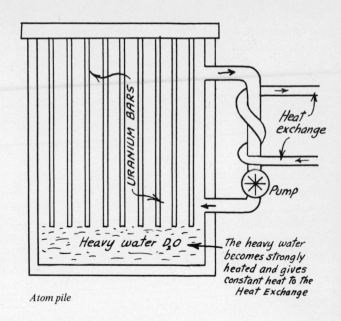

*Atom pile*

*Atom pile used to generate electricity*

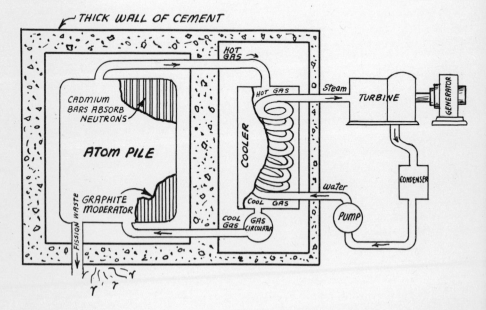

turns the running water inside of them into steam. The water enters the pipe at the bottom and has turned into steam by the time it is pumped to the top. This steam is sent into a turbine which runs an electric generator. As long as the atom pile heats the gas (a time amounting to a couple of decades) it will keep circulating and turning the water into steam to run the generator. The steam that leaves the turbine is condensed back into cool water and sent into the pipes again in a never-ending cycle. In this way the generator can supply us with electric current for years.

One of the most important uses of atomic energy today is in the field of medicine and medical research. If different elements are inserted in the reactor of the atomic piles, the elements become radioactive and give off emanations that have proved to be extremely beneficial in the curing and arresting of certain diseases. These are called radioisotopes.

Radioisotopes have opened up a new field in medical science. They are far more efficient and reliable than chemistry, when it comes to exploring the inner workings of the body. The circulation of the blood can be accurately determined by radioisotopes where it could not have been determined by the old methods of chemical analysis. It is highly possible that such dread diseases as cancer and leukemia will be definitely and permanently cured by radioisotopes, and the human life span may well be increased fifty or a hundred years by the application of these new atomic products to foods and medicines of the future.

# *Other Important Inventions*

# Other Important Inventions

**Adding machine:** In the counting room of a small bank in Auburn, New York, William Seward Burroughs, a bookkeeper with amazing mechanical ability and a passion for inventing, struggled with long columns of figures, preparing to enter their totals in the big ledger. Long hours and poor health drove this shy young inventor to thinking about a machine that would add, and save him and others hours and hours of tedious work. The more he thought about it the more absorbed he became, and in a short time he drew a sketch embodying the basic principles.

After ten years of discouragement, trial-and-error experiments, and nearly $300,000 of speculators' money invested, Burroughs drew finished plans for the first practical adding machine, which was made by the American Arithmometer Co. in St. Louis in 1886. It was not successful at first. The handle, when pulled down too suddenly, affected its accuracy. It had to be pulled forward and then released; and few people could get the knack of it; the public, not knowing how to use the handle, lost confidence. Soon the American Arithmometer Co. was headed for bankruptcy, but Burroughs, with his typical genius for solving difficulties, saved the company by inventing a "dashpot," or governor, which eliminated the handle trouble and made the machine absolutely foolproof. But still it was not bought in quan-

*Burroughs' first adding machine*

*Modern ten-key
Burroughs adding machine*

tities; only 210 were sold in 1895. The public was still skeptical, and it wasn't until Joseph Boyer, an engineer and president of the American Arithmometer Co., developed and made many improvements that the adding machine took hold and started selling. In 1904, 1,000 machines were sold. Today, every bank and business house in the civilized world has one or more adding machines, which save millions of dollars in time and labor annually.

**Air Brake:** Invented by George Westinghouse of Central Bridge, New York, in 1872. In the days before Westinghouse, trains were brought to a stop by a number of brakemen who, in response to a toot from the engine, turned heavy iron wheels on each car

until they slowed the cars down and eventually brought them to rest. So inefficient and ineffectual was this crude method that wrecks were almost as common then as they are scarce today. Because of the great momentum of the moving train, the brakemen, in many cases, didn't have enough strength to stop the cars in time. It was while Westinghouse was in a stalled train, waiting for the wreckage of a train ahead to be cleared, that he thought of a compressed air brake to be applied to each car simultaneously.

The first test run proved successful in a very dramatic manner. Westinghouse, then only twenty-three, got the superintendent of the Pennsylvania Railroad to test his brakes on the Steubenville accommodation train. The little train, consisting of a locomotive and three cars, got up a speed of 30 miles per hour and, as it rounded Grant's Hill, two horses and a cart stopped dead on the crossing, the horses refusing to budge. As the train approached, the engineer, without much faith in the new brakes, applied them and the train came to a full stop about five feet from the horses. This was the first test, and an emergency one, which brought fame to the inventor and established the Westinghouse brakes for all time.

In principle, air compressed to seventy pounds per square inch is sent, by means of pipes under the cars, from the engine to piston boxes located close to the wheels of each car. When the brakes are applied, this compressed air travels through the pipes into the piston boxes, causing the levers to press tightly against the moving wheels, the friction gradually reducing the speed until the train is brought to a full stop. Today all railroads, both here and abroad, are equipped with air brakes based on the Westinghouse principle.

**Balloon:** Like the airplane, the balloon was invented by two brothers, Joseph and Etienne Mongolfier of the little town of Annonay, France. It was early in 1780 that young Joseph startled everyone by jumping off the roof of a six-story house, holding on to a huge canvas umbrella-like device that was the first parachute. He landed safely, and this success started him and his brother on further experiments in the air. A year or so later, while having tea before a huge fireplace, Joseph noticed how smoke rushed up the chimney and took light bits of paper with it. It occurred to him then and there that any bag filled with this hot smoke would go up, and, if there were enough smoke and a big enough bag, it could carry a man along with it. The brothers then made a huge bag and filled it with smoke, only to see it rise and fall as the smoke leaked out. Then Joseph got the idea of carrying a fire under the bag to keep the air in the bag heated, and he and his brother built the "Ad Astra," a huge balloon with a bag thirty-five feet in diameter, carrying 23,000 cubic feet of hot air, and capable of lifting 900 pounds. It was made of packing cloth lined with

heavy paper, and put together with 1,800 buttons and buttonholes. This balloon actually went up, starting to carry Joseph and Etienne with it as they held on to the guide ropes. The following year, 1783, they made a bigger balloon with a basket to carry themselves up high into the air and startle all the spectators. It was then that the balloon became a practical possibility.

**Barometer:** Invented by Italian scientist Torricelli in 1643. Torricelli observed that the pressure of air was strong enough to hold up a column of water in a one-inch-diameter tube to a height of thirty-four feet. He also observed that this height varied with the change of atmospheric pressure and decided that a useful instrument could be made from this. But thirty-four feet of vertical tube was ex-

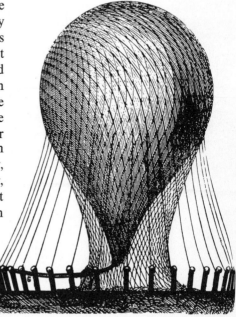

*Early 19th century balloon inflated with hydrogen*

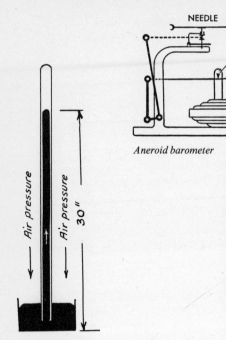

*Aneroid barometer*

*Air pressure*   *Air pressure*   30″

*Mercurial barometer*

tremely impractical, so Torricelli substituted mercury for water. Since mercury is more than thirteen times heavier than water, the column of mercury was held to only twenty-nine inches and, of course, any change in atmospheric pressure varied the height of the mercury in the tube.

If a glass tube a meter (39.37 inches) long is filled to the top with mercury and quickly inverted over a large pot, the mercury will not spill out but will drop in the tube until it stands at 76 centimeters in height and there it will stay. The atmospheric pressure on the mercury in the pot (arrows) presses down with a force exactly equal to the weight of the column of mercury in the tube. Any change in atmospheric pressure, such as occurs when a storm is approach-

ing or on the top of a high mountain, will change the height of the mercury in the tube; by marking graduations on the tube we can determine the changes in atmospheric pressure and predict storms and gauge heights above sea level. Seventy-six centimeters just about equals 30 inches.

The mercurial barometer was the first to be used, but as the demand became more acute the long, heavy glass tube was declared impractical, and the aneroid barometer was invented by M. Vidi of France in 1844 and perfected by J. Goldschmidt of Zurich, Switzerland, in 1860. In this instrument two metal discs, between which air has been partially exhausted, move in and out in accordion fashion as the pressure of the atmosphere changes, and in so doing operate a pointer which signifies on a dial what the change is and what to expect from the weather. The *29, 30,* and *31* on the dial still refer to the height of mercury in the Torricelli tube, even though there is no mercury connected with the aneroid barometer.

**Bicycle:** A two-wheeled vehicle that looked like a bicycle was invented on July 27, 1779, by Baron von Drais of Mannheim-on-Rhine. This was a very queer-looking wooden contrap-

"Ordinary" bicycle

Baron von Drais'
two-wheeled vehicle

"Safety" bicycle

tion with wooden wheels and wooden spokes, not at all like our modern bicycle. It had no gear, no chain, no pedals, and no tires, but it did have a saddle and it could be steered. To ride it one had to straddle it and run, jumping onto the saddle as the wheels gained speed, running again as they slowed.

In 1855 Ernst Michaux, a French locksmith, invented a metal bicycle with a gear, chain, a crank, and pedals, but the machine didn't work very well. In 1859 another Frenchman, a mechanic by the name of Magee, designed a bicycle that became very popular for a while. This was a very large wheel that was pedaled by the rider who sat over it in a high saddle. But, as time went on, one accident after another occurred, some of them quite serious, so the "safety bicycle" was invented in 1866 by Pope. This was essentially the same type that we have today, but it was not until John Dunlop of Scotland invented the pneumatic tire that the bicycle became a vehicle of worldwide use.

**Canning:** It's a pretty big order to name the greatest of all inventions in the entire history of man, but many noted authorities think that the canning of food should have that unusual distinction. Through the canning process man has become entirely and completely independent of seasonal harvests, since canned food is perfectly good year after year and may be shipped in great quantities to any part of the world. Residents of central Africa can enjoy salmon from Oregon; Eskimos can drink orange and grapefruit juices from Florida. Through the invention of canning, people in remote, desert, or flooded regions are fed regardless of the scarcity of growing foods or the damage to crops in those regions. The vast percentage of food consumed by the millions who live in our large cities comes right out of cans.

The inventor of canning was a Paris confectioner by the name of Nicholas Appert, who in 1809 succeeded in preserving food, first in bottles and then in "tin" cans. The basic idea is quite simple. Food must be kept free from the tiny microorganisms which spoil it and make it unfit and unsafe to eat. This is done by heating it to temperatures that destroy bacteria, then cooling it and sealing it in airtight iron cans so that no air can ever get at it. As long as it is packed in this manner it will never spoil, no matter where or how long it is kept. Appert not only succeeded in preserving food in cans but wrote a book on the subject which was published in France in 1810. So great was the impact of this volume that scientific men from every country in the world read it and started preparing and canning hundreds of different kinds of foods. Today the canning industry ranks with the largest in the United States, thanks to the genius of Nicholas Appert, whom most people have never heard of.

**Cellophane:** Invented in 1900 by Jacques F. Brandenberger, a Swiss chemist, and developed in this country by the chemical firm of E. I. Du Pont de Nemours. At first cellophane production was limited and the material was expensive. It was used mainly in the wrapping of luxuries. In 1927 Dr. Hale Charch of the Du Pont staff developed a way to make cellophane thoroughly moistureproof, which made it extremely valuable for the wrapping of foods, cigars, cigarettes, and other items that spoil when exposed to dry heat. The process of manufacture is somewhat like that of papermaking. Wood pulp is ground up and shredded and mixed with caustic soda until it is a pulpy mass. Many different chemicals are then added, and the mixture is put

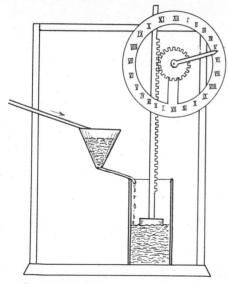

*Roman water clock*

*Galileo's pendulum mechanism*

into a casting machine where acids turn the viscous pulpy stuff into a sheet of transparent cellophane. The sheet is hundreds of feet long and very wide and is rolled up into huge cylinders and stored away.

**Cement:** Invented by Joseph Aspdin of Leeds, England, in 1824. Aspdin was a stonemason seeking a better mortar for his masonry. In his process, limestone is pulverized, burned, mixed with clay and water to make a plastic mass, dried, burned again in a kiln, and finally purified. He was the first to combine these components in their correct proportions and to burn them in a kiln. He called his product Portland cement because it resembled the building stones that were quarried in Portland, England.

**Clock:** The first timepieces were hourglasses and sundials, which later gave way to the water clocks used by the Greeks. In the water clock, a float carrying a rod slowly descended into a tank as the water dripped out drop by drop. Still later, the rod was notched and made to turn a gearwheel, which turned a pointer, thus suggesting the gearwheels and hands of future clocks. Early in the twelfth century water power was discarded in favor of weights, and the first practical clock was constructed in 1360 by Henry de Vick especially for King Charles the Wise of France. This was a huge, massive chunk of machinery run by a 500-pound weight and a gear train, and had only one hand, which marked the hours. It was kept from running down too quickly by a crude escape mechanism consisting of balanced weights on a lever. The de Vick

*Escape mechanism of clock*

clock ran but did not keep accurate time, sometimes losing or gaining two or three hours a day.

It wasn't until Galileo's pendulum, discovered by him in 1581 when he observed the swing of a lamp in the Cathedral of Pisa, was applied to the escape mechanism of Christian Huygens in 1629 that the clock became a useful timepiece. Huygens' invention kept the escape wheel running with remarkable accuracy. A pendulum a meter long vibrated once per second, so that the escape wheel, regulated by the pendulum, was allowed to turn only one notch per second.

In the seventeenth century Dr. Robert Hooke invented the balance spring, the most important invention in the history of timepieces. The balance spring is to the small clock and watch what the pendulum was to the large grandfather clock. It moves in and out, in and out, in and out, in a sort of breathing motion, and in so doing keeps the escape wheel and ratchet ticking for a day or more, and recording time to an unbelievable degree of accuracy. It was also Hooke's idea to replace the weights with a wound-up spring incased on the large gearwheel. As the spring unwound, it transferred its energy to the next wheel, which, in turn, transferred its energy to the next; and so on to the tiny seconds wheel controlled by the hairspring.

The diagram opposite shows the escape mechanism of a clock, an essential part of the works. To understand it, imagine winding a clock where there is no escape mechanism. You wind the big hour-hand wheel, which is attached to the mainspring, and this wheel is geared to the minute-hand wheel, which in turn is geared to the seconds-hand wheel. For every revolution of the hour wheel there are 60 revolutions of the minute wheel and 3,600 revolutions of the seconds wheel, so you can see how the little seconds wheel would whiz around as the clock slowly runs down. It would take about two minutes for this to happen. When the rapidly whirling seconds wheel is connected to this escape mechanism the ratchet above it keeps it from whizzing around, since each notch is taken in turn in the well-known "tick-tock" movement. By calculation, this wheel turns so as to allow the seconds wheel attached to it to make one revolution in a minute, and this in turn allows the minute wheel to make one revolution in an hour.

**Cotton gin:** Patented by Eli Whitney of Westboro, Massachusetts, on

*Eli Whitney watching the working of the cotton gin*

*The original cotton gin*

March 14, 1794. After graduating from Yale in 1792, Whitney spent the summer on the plantation of Nathanael Greene in Savannah, Georgia. It was while watching the farm hands at work that he got the idea for the cotton gin. His first crude model was a wooden cylinder and a number of rotating spikes set one-half inch apart and almost touching a wire sieve. The sieve sifted out cotton seeds while the rotating spikes pulled the cotton lint through in a continuous thread. All excess lint deposited on the spikes was cleaned by revolving brushes.

Whitney's first model was so efficient that it did in one hour the day's work of several men. It made such a commotion among the farmers that, before Whitney could patent it, it was pirated, and farmers everywhere were using the new timesaving machine without paying any royalties to Whitney.

**Elevator:** The invention of the elevator is credited to Leonardo da Vinci, and the first elevator is in the Cathedral in Milan, where once a year it is "unwrapped" and run from the street floor to the roof. It is a delicate birdcage affair, one of the many wonderful inventions of the genius whose "Last Supper" graces the walls of the Church of Santa Maria delle Grazie in that city.

In the early seventeenth century, Velayer, a French architect, invented the first passenger elevator with a counterweight to balance it as it moved up and down. It was called "the flying chair" and operated by man power furnished by servants.

The first practical elevators were hydraulic. They were operated by water power. A long plunger, extending downward into the ground as far as the building was high, moved through water, which was forced into the deep hole or removed from it according to the direction of travel of the car. It was controlled by a hand rope extending through the car.

The inventor of the modern elevator was Elisha G. Otis, who in 1852 took out the first patent on a safety-type car which could not possibly fall. The first advertisement for this elevator appeared in a leaflet in 1855 and the first elevator sold was at 275 Hudson St., New York City, in 1853. The first passenger elevator in the United States with this safety device was installed March 23, 1857, in the store of E. V. Haughwout & Co. in New York by Otis. It was driven by steam and had a speed of 40 feet per minute.

By 1880 the electric motor was developed to a point where it was used for a great many purposes, and soon afterward, the electric elevator appeared in the taller buildings. Since then there have been numerous improvements on the elevator, and today almost all cars are electrically operated.

In 1894 the first recorded operatorless (push-button) elevator was installed by Otis in the New York residence of Mrs. E. I. Shepard. In 1924 the first Signal Control elevators were installed by Otis in the Standard Oil Building in New York. The first automatic and electronic supervisory system (Autotronic) was developed by the Otis Company in 1948 for intensive operation of a group of elevators. Among the first installations were

*An early Otis elevator*

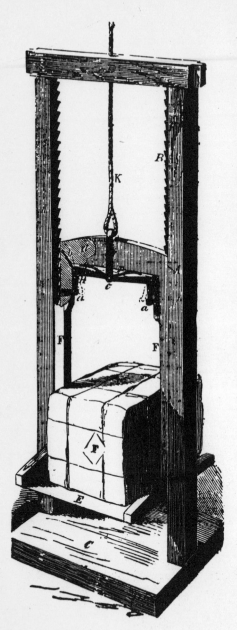

*The mechanical basis of the elevator, showing platform and stops to prevent slipping*

those in the United Nations Secretariat Building and 100 Park Avenue, New York. And, in 1950, the first group-supervised, intensive-service elevators, *without attendants in the cars,* were completed by the Otis Company at the Atlantic Refining Company Building in Dallas, Texas.

**Gas lighting:** Invented by William Murdoch, of Scotland, in 1792. The first city to illuminate its streets by gas was London in 1807.

**The half-tone process** is entirely responsible for the reproduction of photographs in newspapers and magazines. It was invented by Frederick Eugene Ives, of Litchfield, Connecticut, and is one of the most important inventions of modern times. There is quite a difference between printing a photograph from a negative on light-sensitive Velox and printing it in ink from a metal plate in a printing press. Prior to the invention of the half-tone process there was no known way of doing this. Ives, who was an expert photographer with a flair for inventing, made numerous photographs on metal plates, but each time he inked the plates and printed them on paper he got a black smudge and nothing more. It was in the summer of 1878, at Cornell University, that he hit upon the idea of breaking up the photograph by means of a screen. He photographed the picture with a fine screen in front of the camera. This divided the photograph into tiny squares and dots which, when transferred to a metal plate and placed into an acid bath, became raised and separated as the acid ate in between them, wherever the lines of the screen appeared. The

*Cyrus H. McCormick*

*The McCormick reaper,*
*patented in 1834*

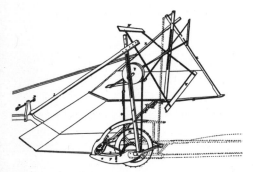

*McCormick's 1847 reaper*

varying degrees of light and shade on the original picture are thus accounted for in the size and separation of the dots and squares. You can test this by examining any newspaper photograph with a good magnifying glass. The idea of the screen breaking up the photograph into dots and squares is the half-tone process that is used to reproduce photographs in every newspaper and most magazines and books throughout the entire world. The first practical use made of it was in Philadelphia in February 1881.

**Harvester (reaper):** Invented by Obed Hussey, of Maryland, and Cyrus McCormick, of Virginia, each unknown to the other. Hussey's invention is dated June 21, 1834, and McCormick's is dated December 31, 1833. While the two types of reapers were different, each was important. Hussey's had a reciprocating saw-toothed cutter sliding within double-guard fingers and driven by a crankshaft operated by gears from the main drive wheel. The operator rode on the rear platform. McCormick's machine was pushed by a team of horses hitched behind the cutting and dividing apparatus.

**Incandescent lamp:** Invented by Thomas A. Edison on October 21, 1879. Edison was convinced that a wire-thin piece of high resistance material would glow when a current was sent through it in a vacuum. He made hundreds of fruitless experiments, sending current through platinum wire and zirconium and almost a thousand different materials inside glass bulbs from which most of the air had been exhausted. He finally found the answer in carbonized cotton thread in the form of a loop. This he sealed into a bulb and sent a current through it; it gave a lasting dull glow. The moderate success of this experiment convinced Edison that carbon was the material he should use, so after many months of intensive research, he found a certain type of bamboo which filled the bill. Edison then wired the village of Menlo Park, New Jersey, and on December 31, 1879, demonstrated the lamp with lights in houses, on the streets, and in his laboratory, supplied with electricity from a single source. It took two more years to supply New York City, because Edison wished to use underground mains. In September 1882, he opened a generating station in Pearl Street, New York, the first electric utility. It was then that "bottled light" became a reality, and the wizard of Menlo Park lighted the world. In 1913 Coolidge invented the tungsten filament which is the standard bulb used today.

**Lathe:** The mechanic's lathe was the brain child of Henry Maudslay, an English inventor, in 1797. To Maudslay, more than any other man, we owe our modern precision machinery, on which mechanics work to an accuracy of one ten-thousandth of an inch. Without the lathe this kind of precision would be impossible, and cars and airplanes, generators and motors, and all of the other high-precision machinery could not exist.

**Loom:** The history of weaving and the various improvements on the methods of producing cloth and textiles is extremely long, reaching back to an-

*Edison bamboo-filament copper-plated lamps*

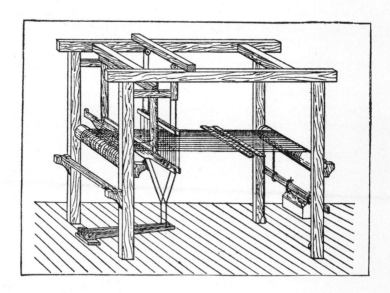

*Diagram of a hand loom*

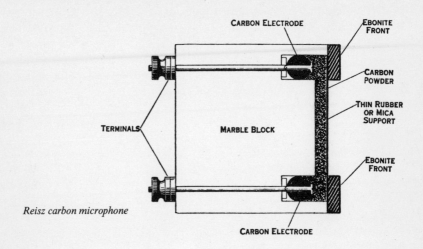

CARBON ELECTRODE

EBONITE FRONT

CARBON POWDER

THIN RUBBER OR MICA SUPPORT

TERMINALS

MARBLE BLOCK

EBONITE FRONT

CARBON ELECTRODE

*Reisz carbon microphone*

tiquity and even before. The first practical loom, known as the spinning jenny, was invented by three men independently of one another in 1769. These men were James Hargraves, Richard Arkwright, and Samuel Crompton. The spinning jenny was a hand-operated loom incapable of turning out textiles in great quantities. In 1785 Edmund Cartwright, a clergyman in the Church of England, invented the first power loom, and in 1789 commenced to make all kinds of fabrics and textiles at Dorchester, England. In 1792 Cartwright added new parts to his loom, which included a number of shuttle boxes that enabled him to weave checks, cross stripes, and other designs into the cloth. Ten years later William Radcliff made a number of improvements on the Cartwright loom, and from then on one improvement after an-

other produced the present-day loom, which is one of the most complicated and important machines of modern times.

**Match:** It is very difficult to believe that the common match, which many of us use many times every day, was invented in the nineteenth century. It is so much a part of our present civilization that it seems to have been with us for hundreds of years; but the fact is that John Walker, a druggist of Stockton-on-Tees, England, invented it in 1827. He dipped thin strips of wood into a mixture of antimony sulfide, potassium chlorate,

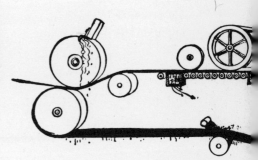

*Fourdrinier paper machine*

and glue, and produced a crude match which ignited after hard rubbing on sandpaper.

There was no phosphorus in Walker's match, and it wasn't until Dr. Charles Sauria, of St. Lothair, France, and A. D. Phillips, in the United States, added that important element that the match became valuable. Sauria increased the amount of sulfur, so the match could be ignited merely by striking it once or twice on a rough surface. The common match today contains phosphorus, sulfur, and a chemical rich in oxygen, like potassium chlorate ($KClO_3$). This mixture is sealed onto the stick of the match with glue in order to keep the phosphorus from igniting when exposed to the air. As soon as the match is struck and the glue rubbed off, the phosphorus is exposed to the air and it ignites and is further helped by the potassium chlorate, which furnishes more oxygen. This all takes place quickly, but the intense heat ignites the wood of the stick and the match burns. The wood is treated with a chemical which prevents any afterglow when the match is extinguished.

**Microphone:** Invented by Thomas A. Edison in 1877. Edison improved the Bell telephone by inventing the carbon-granule transmitter, and it is this transmitter in a more sensitive form that is the radio microphone. Edison used low-resistance carbon grains to vary the current and cause extremely small fluctuations in the circuit. The patent (No. 474230) was not granted until 1892 because of interference with the Berliner patent, which was essentially the same.

**Paper, mass production:** Invented by Louis Robert. By his method, rags were ground up and beaten by a revolving beater. This pulpy mass, screened and diluted with water, was then piped into a huge metal box and allowed to flow out in a thin stream onto a continuously moving screen of #70 mesh wire. As the pulp passed from the box to the screen, the particles of fiber floated together and interlaced with one another because of the additional zigzag motion of the

*Paper pulp beating machine*

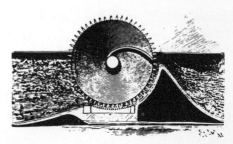

screen. Meanwhile the water was strained off, and the moist pulpy mass was compressed and flattened by heavy rollers into a smooth, long sheet.

Robert's invention was developed in England by the Fourdrinier brothers and was known as the Fourdrinier process. It made paper from rags only, and, since the demand for more and more paper increased, it was evident that a time would come when there would not be enough rags available. René de Reaumur, a native of La Rochelle in France, had suggested a remedy, but his suggestion went unheeded for years. Reaumur was a naturalist whose whole life was devoted to the study of insects. In the course of his intensive study of wasps he was able to prove that the wasp's nest was nothing more than crude paper actually manufactured by the insect. Reaumur decided that the wasp produced this paper by the combination of certain chemicals in its body with wood from the branches of trees and bushes. If the wasp can make paper from wood, why couldn't man? At a meeting of French scientists in Paris in 1719, he read a paper which advised his colleagues to "look to the wasp" for the most practical way to produce paper.

It is remarkable that the lesson of the wasp was not taken seriously until the nineteenth century, and all Reaumur's researches had to wait that long before development. As late as 1868, nearly one hundred and fifty years after Reaumur's paper was read, the wood-pulp process was begun. In this process wood is cut up into fine chips, which are treated with numerous acids and chemicals and put through a highly complicated process of washing and screening, basically the same as that invented by Robert.

**Phonograph:** Invented by Thomas A. Edison in 1878. It is an interesting fact that the telegraph, invented by Morse in 1832, not only introduced the world to the enormous possibilities of the electromagnet, but it gave Bell the idea for the telephone and Edison the idea for the phonograph. It was while Edison was working on the repeating and embossing telegraph, which he patented in 1874, that the idea of the phonograph came to him. Edison's telegraph repeater was a disc of paper revolving on a metal disc directly below an electromagnet on a pivoted arm.

The machine, which looked like the forerunner of the phonograph of today, was used for transmitting telegraph messages very rapidly, and it was while Edison was testing the various speeds of the revolving paper disc that he noticed a faint musical note coming from the machine. Most inventors would not have given this a second thought; but Edison did. Knowing full well that sound is vibration, he examined the pivoted magnet and the embossing point. Edison made further experiments, reversing the process by running the paper disc quickly under the embossing needle after that needle had made the dot-and-dash indentations. This time the note was unmistakably clear. It was immediately obvious to Edison that the indentations caused the needle to vibrate and make the sound. Perhaps

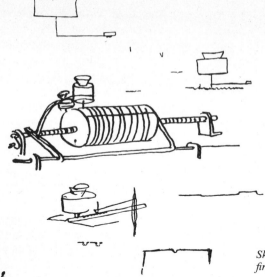

*Sketch of Edison's
first phonograph, 1877*

Kreusi
Make this Edison
Aug 12/77

*The first phonograph*

*Second form of phonograph*

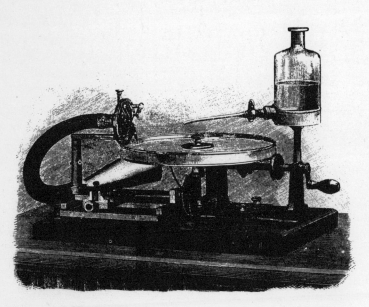

*The Gramophone recorder*

*Edison's Standard Phonograph*

he could make a needle vibrate with his own voice, and in so doing produce tiny indentations in something soft which, if run under the needle again, would play back his voice.

Edison made a rough sketch, which he handed to his assistant with orders to "make this." When it was made Edison added a horn and made an "Oooh" sound into the machine. After a few more models with tinfoil as the recording medium, Edison recited the nursery rhyme "Mary Had a Little Lamb" into the horn, so the first words ever spoken by a machine came back in Edison's own voice. Edison patented this crude machine in 1878 and kept on improving it. He did away with the hand crank, substituting a motor driven by a spring. He dispensed with the tinfoil and used wax cylinders. The Edison gramophone was marketed in 1901.

For three years the old wax records were used with the up-and-down method of cutting for recording. In 1904 Emile Berliner, a German scientist, invented the lateral cut, and the flat disc records became the standard records we have today.

**Pistol:** Who the actual inventor of the pistol was is not definitely known; perhaps it was the work of many men. One thing is sure: it was born of necessity, for there was a great need for a firearm that could be discharged with only one hand, leaving the other free for use of defense or for another weapon. The first pistols were very crude affairs.

For more than 500 years inventors have been improving the pistol. The best-known inventor in this connection was Samuel Colt, who is credited with the invention of the revolver. The fundamental principle of the revolving chamber on firearms was

*Single and double action
six shooter pistols*

known long before Colt, but he really perfected it and made the modern revolver a practical weapon.

Colt took out a patent on February 25, 1836, for "a single-barrel pistol having a many-chambered rotating breech which turned, locked, and unlocked by cocking." This invention also applied to rifles, and the Patent Arms Manufacturing Co. was formed the following year to make Colt firearms. Colt firearms were first used in the Seminole Indian War of 1837.

**Radar:** On June 24, 1930, some U. S. Naval Research Laboratory scientists at Anacostia, a suburb of Washington, D. C., while working on high-frequency blind-landing systems at Bolling Field, noticed that patterns of waves showed interference only when planes passed through the influenced area. This led to plane detection by means of radio-beam reflection, and the new science was called "radar." Lieutenant Hyland of the Anacostia Naval Air Station made further experiments in 1931 and showed that quickly intermittent radio beams sent out in all directions not only told of the location of planes but could give their distance from the observer and their shape. On August 12, 1932, the Radio Corporation of America started to develop radar, and today it is one of the most important tools for defense. In radar sudden pulsations of short waves are sent out in all directions, and their echo, or their reflection, after bouncing off all objects in their path (from 25 to 250,000 miles) is caught in a large rotating dishpanlike contraption. Since these pulsations travel with the speed of light and the time interval between the sending and the echo is so short it has to be measured in millionths of a second, the radar screen must be operated by means of a cathode beam, which is the only possible way of recording such velocities. The radar screen is quite similar to the television screen described in part 6, Chapter VI.

**Rubber:** After a lifetime of discouragement and dire poverty, Charles Goodyear of New Haven, Connecticut, was rewarded. On June 15, 1844, the first basic patent on the vulcanizing of rubber was issued to him. It is doubtful whether any other inventor went through so many years of hardship and near starvation to accomplish the seemingly impossible. Without the slightest knowledge of the chemistry of what he was doing, Goodyear tried combining everything that he could get his hands on with the soft, sticky, unusable rubber as it came from the rubber tree. It was early in 1844, after ten years of heartbreaking experimenting, that a mixture of natural rubber, sulfur, and white lead actually hardened on the old potbelly stove in Goodyear's home and gave him the clue to the vulcanizing process. The fact that heat from the sun affected natural rubber, making it softer and stickier than usual, while the heat from his stove did just the reverse, had great significance for Goodyear, who noted carefully the exact temperature at which the mixture hardened. Further experiments and research enabled him to produce an amazing new material which stretched, was resilient, an excellent insulator, waterproof, and unaffected by either heat or cold. It proved to be the one ideal material for automobile tires, electrical insulators, waterproof wearing apparel, medical equipment, and hundreds of other products.

**Safety pin:** Invented on April 10, 1849 by Walter Hunt, an amazing young man with scores of practical ideas. Among Hunt's repertoire of inventions, in addition to the sewing machine, we find all kinds of improvements on firearms, ice plows, paraffin

*Safety pin and Roman fibula*

candles, velocipedes, and machinery for making nails and rivets. J. R. Chapin, Hunt's friend and a draftsman, tells how he paid a fifteen-dollar debt by *inventing the safety pin!* According to Chapin, Hunt took an old piece of wire and kept twisting it into various forms until, in only three hours, he had made the first perfect and practical safety pin, which he patented and sold outright to a manufacturer for only $400.

**Shade roller:** On October 11, 1864, Stewart Hartshorne, an engineer of Short Hills, New Jersey, obtained a basic patent on a spring-operated shade roller with a ratchet catching mechanism that would hold the shade stationary at any desired height just by giving it a slight tug. It also rolled the shade up when given a slight tug and, in so doing, rewound the spring inside the roller. This amazingly clever little device, no larger than a peanut, made the window shade a practical thing, and nearly every window shade everywhere throughout the world today is equipped with a shade roller on which Stewart Hartshorne had the basic patent. The only window shades that do not use the Hartshorne idea are

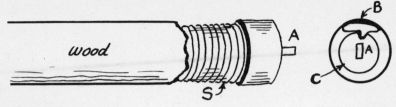

*Shade roller mechanism*

Venetian blinds. Inside that little metal cap on one end of the wooden roller to which the shade is fastened, is attached a long spring $S$ which is attached to the projecting piece $A$. $A$ is a tiny rectangular piece which fits into the shade holder and is held there securely. When the shade is pulled down the projecting piece $A$ remains still while the spring inside the roller goes round and round and, in so doing, winds itself up. If the shade is released it immediately flies up to the top as the spring unwinds, but if it is given a slight tug a little catch $B$ (shown in the end view) drops down and engages in the notch on $C$, which is the top of the long spring. This halts the motion and keeps the spring from unwinding. Another little tug and you automatically push $B$ up enough to disengage $C$ and the shade goes up. It's all a question of little tugs which affect $B$ and keep the spring from winding or unwinding.

**Steel, Bessemer process:** In spite of the thousands of articles made from aluminum, steel takes first place in usefulness and importance. Without steel there could be no tall buildings, no bridges or large construction of any kind, no cutlery or tools of any

practical use, and no modern machinery. Steel is both cheap and plentiful—the number-one metal in all industry—and while certain kinds of steel were known before 1856, they were far too expensive to manufacture for the wide variety of uses demanded of that metal today. Prior to 1856 the two metals most commonly used were cast and wrought iron. Cast iron was perfectly suited for taking compression, but because of its high carbon content it was too brittle to withstand shock or high tension. Wrought iron, on the other hand, because of the absence of carbon in it, was useful in taking shock and strain, but was far too soft to be practical.

A type of iron midway between these two was badly needed, and it remained for Sir Henry Bessemer, a British engineer from Hertfordshire, England, to invent it in 1856. His process was to decarbonize cast iron by forcing air through the molten hot metal. In this way he removed the carbon and silicon and other impurities, and at the same time produced a flame much hotter than any that had been produced before. After the brilliant fiery mass of decarbonized cast iron had attained a certain tem-

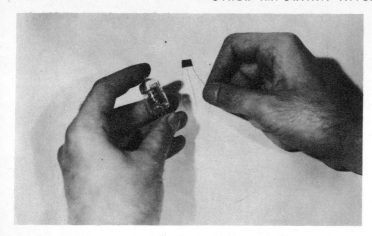

*Transistor, the tiny
bit of germanium
that works electrical
wonders*

perature, he added *spiegeleisen,* a mixture of manganese, iron, and some carbon, to the burning liquid and lowered the temperature. There was just enough carbon and manganese in the mixture to make it extremely hard, yet there was not enough to make it brittle. When it cooled and hardened it was steel, the kind that is the basis of all the different types of steel used today.

Bessemer erected steel works at Sheffield, England, the city that is and always will be associated with steel. He manufactured it for years, improving on it each year and enabling it to be produced at a cost of about one cent per pound. So vital to science and invention was the Bessemer process that the *Scientific American* classed it as the most important invention of the latter half of the nineteenth century, and Queen Victoria knighted Bessemer in 1879.

**Tires:** Invented in 1888 by John Boyd Dunlop, of Dreghorn in Ayrshire, Scotland. In 1887 he constructed a handmade tire for his son's tricycle.

It was the first practical pneumatic tire, and it proved so useful that Dunlop patented it on December 7, 1888. In 1890 the Pneumatic Tyre and Boothe Cycle Agency was formed in Belfast, and tires were manufactured on a small scale.

**Transistor:** On June 30, 1948, Doctors John Bardeen and Walter Brattain of the Bell Laboratories in New York announced their invention of the transistor. This device, no bigger than a shoelace tip, is capable of doing practically all of the things that the vacuum tube does and many things which it doesn't do. It may, in time, take the place of the vacuum tube just as the automobile has taken the place of the old horse-and-buggy.

Although the transistor can do all the things done by the vacuum tube, it is not a vacuum tube. It has no cathode, no grid, no plate, and is not a tube at all. Yet it is an excellent rectifier, amplifier, and oscillator, and it fills many other vital roles in modern industry. It works instantly, without any warm-up delay, at the point of contact, and consumes about a thousandth of the current required to light an ordinary flashlight, yet some types can amplify an electric sign 100,000 times. For this reason, it is much more convenient and much less expensive than a vacuum tube. It is being used more and more in radio and television sets, long-distance telephone circuits, hearing aids, signal devices, and government equipment. The transistor is gradually making it possible to dial *directly* any number in the United States from any other telephone, without the aid of the long-distance operator. The experiment was done successfully at Englewood, New Jersey, and is being extended to other towns and cities.

The regular transistor is nothing more than two thin wires spread a few thousandths of an inch apart on a "wafer" of the rare element germanium. Another type, invented by Dr. William Shockley of the Bell Laboratories, consists of an extremely small sandwich of germanium, treated so that its alternate layers have different electrical properties and its center is pure germanium. This little instrument occupies only one four-hundredth of an inch.

The basic theory of the transistor is very involved and technical. It has to do with semiconductors, which are extremely rare and have been investigated only for the last ten years.

In semiconductors like silicon and germanium, there are extremely few current-carrying electrons, perhaps only one for every million atoms; but oddly enough this number, small as it is, can be varied a thousand times or more by changing the electronic structure of the materials through the influence of an electric field from the outside.

To make this concept clearer, all we need to do is investigate the atom a little more thoroughly. Electrons in nonconductors revolve around the nucleus of the atom in various orbits or rings traveling so fast they form what is called "electron shells," which by virtue of their great velocity and consequent high energy keep to themselves and do not wander off to flow along and form a current. In these nonconductors, the electron shell, or valence band, is widely separated from the conduction band, and enormous energy is necessary to boost an electron from its electron shell to this band of conduction. In a conductor (almost any metal) this electron shell or valence band overlaps the conduction band, and the electrons flow very readily along the conducting metal.

In a semiconductor like germanium, the electrons in the valence band are not near the conduction band, but the slightest outside stimulus can boost them up to it. Ordinary room temperature, for example, can kick many of the electrons in the germanium atom up to the conduction band and, in doing so, leave what physicists call "holes" in the places they vacated. These holes carry positive charges and, of course, invite electrons from outside sources. The holes not only receive the incoming electrons, but they, themselves, move toward the conduction band and, in so doing, create a current, as well as carrying electrons in that current.

The slightest outside stimulus starts "holes" moving in the semisolid—holes that are left by electrons which have escaped into the conduction band. These moving holes, in addition to carrying a current of their own, carry electrons which have been sent into the germanium from an outside source and so increase the current. To quote from a news release put out by the Bell Laboratories on July 1, 1948:

"Transistor action depends upon the fact that electrons in a semiconductor can carry current in two distinctly different ways. This is because most of the electrons in a semiconductor do not contribute to carrying the current at all. Instead they are held in fixed positions and act as a rigid cement to bind together the atoms in a solid. Only if one of these electrons gets out of place, or if another electron is introduced in one of a number of ways, can current be carried. If, on the other hand, one of the electrons normally present in the cement is removed, then the 'hole' left behind it can move like a bubble in a liquid and thus carry current.

"In a transistor made of a semiconductor, which normally conducts only by the extra electron process, current flows easily into the input point, which is at a low positive voltage, and out of the output point, which is at a higher negative voltage. The area of interaction is produced by 'holes' introduced by the input current and collected by the output point."

**Water closet:** If you have ever visited Williamsburg, Virginia, and have gone through the rebuilt and restored colonial section, you will probably remember the magnificent furniture and draperies in the Governor's Palace and the dazzling splendor of the ballroom reflecting the luxurious living of the rich in those pre-Revolutionary days.

But you suddenly realize an amazing thing about all colonial houses, extremely wealthy as well as wretchedly poor; they had no bathrooms. The rich and the poor alike had no such thing as running water in their homes. There were no bathtubs, and no toilets. The wealthy had slaves to pump water for the morning washing and shaving but had to go to an out-

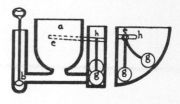

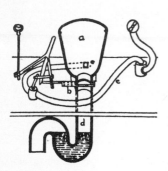

*Early flush actions
for water closets*

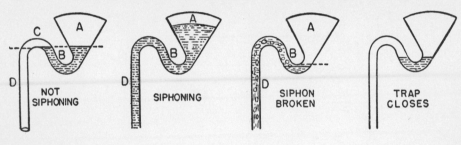

*Siphon action in water trap*

side privy or "necessary house" in lieu of a toilet. The invention of the water closet was yet to come, and the lack of that now common and vitally important fixture was an underlying cause of the plagues and epidemics, like typhoid and cholera and smallpox. The filth and foul odors of those days resulted in most people dying before they reached the age of fifty.

The invention of the water closet has made community living much safer. Without it there could be no apartment houses, hotels, office buildings, or other places where people live or work in large numbers. Most of us fail to realize this; practically everyone takes the modern toilet for granted. We use it and flush it every day of our lives, never thinking of the hundreds of millions of lives it has saved in the very short time it has been in use.

The water closet was invented in 1775 by Alexander Cummings, a watchmaker of Bond Street, London. Cummings' water closet used a sliding valve, but, more important, was the very first to apply a trap, really the essential part of any sanitary toilet. The invention of Cummings was followed by more than sixty patented improvements in the

next hundred years. The patent offices both here and abroad are filled with plans for improvements on water closets, each new patent keeping up with the advancement of plumbing and sanitation. The modern water closet, or toilet, was born on April 15, 1890, when a patent was granted to C. A. Neff for a siphon type of bowl. Since then, many improvements have been made, until today a perfectly operating toilet is a positive necessity in every home, office, and public building.

The working of the modern toilet is extremely simple, and based entirely on the principle of the siphon. To understand it consider the four diagrams shown above. In figure *1* water is poured into a funnel with a curved pipe, the trap, and it stays in the curved portion as shown. Now see what happens when we fill up the funnel as in figure *2*. The added weight of water pushes the water in the trap up to the curve and *down the long soil pipe* and, as long as water flows into the funnel, this will continue. But when the water stops flowing into the funnel the siphonic action is broken as in figure *3* and some of the water slides back into the trap as shown in figure *4*. A very light flow

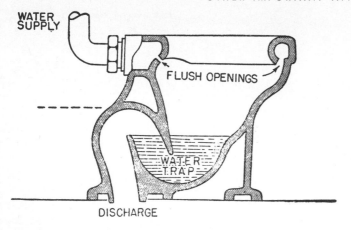

*Water closet, showing how*
*water flushes into the bowl*
*and down through the trap*

*Mechanism within the tank: as*
*the water flows out through* D, *the*
*ball sinks and opens valve* F

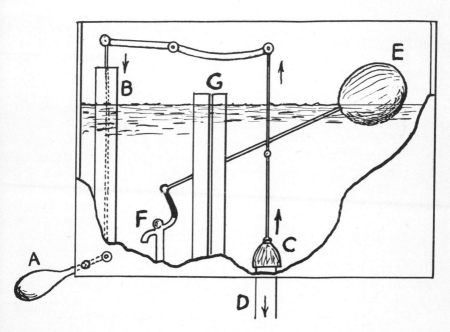

of water fills the level of the trap to where it was in figure *1,* and the fixture is ready to operate again. Now see the diagram on page 259 of the modern siphon bowl toilet. You will see at once how it works and how the heavy rush of water into the bowl when you pull the handle causes a strong siphonic action which sucks all the waste matter in the bowl down the soil pipe into the sewer without the faintest odor or danger of contamination.

Within the tank, there is an ingenious mechanism to release the water and control its flow back into the tank. When the knob *A* is pulled up, the long rod in *B* moves down and consequently the thin rod at the other end moves up, lifting the rubber cap or ball *C.* The water in the tank then flows out and down the pipe *D* into the bowl of the toilet causing the siphonic action just described. As the water in the tank runs out, the floating metal ball *E* moves down with it and, in doing so, it opens up the faucet *F* allowing water to enter the tank. Now knob *A* is back in place and consequently the rubber cap *C* is over the pipe again so no water runs out, and water is constantly flowing in through *F.* As the water rises, so does the metal ball *E,* and when it gets to a certain height it automatically shuts off the faucet *F* and the tank is filled once more. The pipe *G* is there in case too much water flows into the tank; it connects with *D* and allows the water to run out into the bowl.

**X-ray tube:** Discovered by Professor W. K. Roentgen, of the Royal University of Würzburg, Germany. Knowing little about these remarkable rays, and not being able to analyze them completely, he called them by the algebraic unknown "x". When two metal terminals are sealed into a tube from which air has been exhausted and a current is sent from one terminal to the other, the whole tube glows with a rosy light and electrons pour from the negative or cathode to the positive or anode.

The flow of electrons in this cathode tube, when focused on a platinum or tungsten target, actually bombards the target, and this bombardment of electrons produce a ray with great penetrating powers known as the X ray. The ray will penetrate any material composed of atoms containing comparatively few electrons, neutrons, and protons—the lighter elements. Atoms become heavier and more complicated as electrons, neutrons, and protons are added. The light atoms have fewer electrons, etc., and become transparent to the X rays, while the heavier atoms, like lead, platinum, gold, iridium, etc., prevent the penetration of these rays. Since human flesh is composed of oxygen, hydrogen, and carbon atoms, it becomes transparent to the rays, but bones, which are composed of calcium and phosphorus atoms, shut out X rays. As a matter of fact, the bones which show up in an X-ray negative do not appear nearly so black as a piece of lead, which shows that the composition of the heavier atoms has the greater opacity. It follows that any carbohydrate or hydrocarbon—any living tissue—will be transparent to X rays, while any metal with appreciable density will be opaque.

The X-ray camera is placed directly above the area to be photographed, while the photographic plate is placed directly underneath. The rays are invisible to the eye but not to the plate. When the photographic plate is developed, we get a sort of shadow picture of the bony structure of the human body, the location of foreign matter, or of organs that have been chemically prepared to show up on the X ray. X rays are also used widely in industry to detect flaws in metal, etc.

**Zipper:** The Zipper, or hookless fastener as it used to be called, was invented by two men: Whitcomb L. Judson, of Chicago, and Gideon Sundback, of Hoboken, New Jersey. Judson took out a patent in 1896 on two metal chains brought together by the movement of a small metal slider, which was the forerunner of the modern zipper. Sundback greatly improved this by using the familiar notching device on cloth or leather and thereby produced one of the most useful locking devices of modern times. The Zipper was patented by Sundback in 1913, and it is now manufactured by the Talon Hookless Fastener Co. Similar devices, under different names, are made by a number of other firms.

# What Are the Fifteen Greatest Inventions of All Time?

Selecting fifteen of the greatest inventions of all time is no easy task, since any such choice is generally a matter of opinion and no list will completely satisfy everyone. But, defining "invention" as *the practical application of known principles to new and useful purposes,* here are what I consider the fifteen greatest inventions in the entire history of mankind:

*The four basic principles on which all machinery runs*

1. The **wheel**
2. The **lever**
3. The **wedge**
4. The **screw**

5. The **smelting** of metals

6. **Written communication**

7. **Weaving**

8. **Movable type**—without which 98 per cent of all the people in the world who are now educated would be ignorant

9. The **microscope**—responsible for the elimination of plagues and epidemics and the curing of diseases

10. **Canning**—enabling man to store perishable food indefinitely

11. The **calculus**—the most powerful tool in the mathematical sciences and the basis of all branches of engineering

12. The **internal combustion engine**

*Vital to every electrical invention in the world today*

13. The **electromagnet**

14. The **vacuum tube**

and

15. The **hydrogen bomb**—the ghastly destructive power of this invention will eliminate war forever

# Acknowledgments

The author and The World Publishing Company herewith thank the following institutions whose courtesy has made possible the preparation of the *World Book of Great Inventions.*

All possible care has been taken to trace the ownership of every illustration included and to make full acknowledgment for its use. If any errors have accidentally occurred they will be corrected in subsequent editions, provided notification is sent to the publisher.

Abelard-Schuman, Inc., for illustrations on pages 45, 61, from *Man the Maker,* by R. J. Forbes. Copyright 1950 by Abelard-Schuman, Inc.

Aeronautical Museum, Smithsonian Institution, for illustrations on pages 112, 113, 115, 119, 120.

American Airlines Inc., for an illustration on page 120.

American Telephone & Telegraph Company, for illustrations on pages 165, 168, 169, 172, 173, 174, 175, 176, 177, 180, 181.

American Type Founders Sales Corp., for illustrations on pages 49, 50, 51.

Bell Telephone Laboratories, Inc., for illustrations on pages 155, 157, 255.

Burroughs Corporation, for illustrations on pages 231, 232.

Chanticleer Company, Inc., for illustrations on page 124, from *Rockets and Jets,* by Marie Neurath. Published by Lothrop, Lee & Shepard Company, Inc.

Cinerama Inc., for the illustration on page 91.

Crown Publishers, Inc., for an illustration on page 213, from *The New High Fidelity Handbook,* by Irving Greene and James Radcliffe. Revised edition copyright 1955 by Crown Publishers, Inc.

Dodd, Mead & Company, for the illustration on page 57, from a wash drawing by Russell W. Porter in *Glass Giant of Palomar,* by David Woodbury. Copyright 1948 by Dodd, Mead & Company.

Doubleday & Company, Inc., for illustrations on pages 19, 92, 93, 94, 104, 105, 106, from *The Turning Wheel,* by Arthur Pound. Copyright 1934 by Doubleday & Company, Inc.

George Eastman House, for illustrations on pages 77, 78, 81, 82.

Thomas Alva Edison Foundation Museum, West Orange, New Jersey, for illustrations on pages 88, 156, 164, 184, 249, 250.

Encyclopaedia Britannica Inc., for illustrations on pages 27, 102, 245, 246.

General Motors Corporation, for illustrations on pages 107, 108, 109.

Harper & Brothers, Publishers, for the illustrations of the Mark Twain letter on page 64. Copyright by Harper & Brothers, Publishers.

R. Hoe & Company, Inc., for the illustration on page 48.

Mergenthaler Linotype Company, for illustrations on pages 39, 40, 41, 42, 44.

Munn & Company, for illustrations on pages 43, 46, 47, 86, 87, 89, 150, 151, 152, 153, 154, 246, 247, from *Progress of Invention in the Nineteenth Century,* by Byrn.

New York Central System, for illustrations on pages 99, 110.

New York Public Library Picture Collection, for illustrations on pages 22, 24, 25, 30, 32, 33, 34, 35, 36, 37, 95, 116.

W. W. Norton & Company, Inc., for illustrations on pages 96, 97, 98, from *Iron Horses,* by Edwin P. Alexander. Copyright 1941 by W. W. Norton & Company, Inc.

Otis Elevator Company, for illustrations on pages 241, 242.

Radio Corporation of America, for the illustration on page 209.

Remington Rand Inc., for illustrations on pages 59, 60, 62, 63, 65.

Science Digest for an illustration on page 129.

Singer Sewing Machine Company, for illustrations on pages 66, 67, 68, 70, 71, 72, 73, 74, 75.

Smithsonian Institution, for illustrations on pages 145, 186, 188, 189, 245.

Underwood Corp., for an illustration on page 65.

United States Navy, for illustrations on pages 183, 185, 186, 187, 190, 192, 194.

Western Union Telegraph Company, for illustrations on pages 161, 162, 163.

# Index

Figures in italics indicate illustrations

Abacus, 26–27; *27*
Adding machine, 231–232; *231, 232*
Aerodynamics, principles of, 111–113, 118–125; *113, 114, 122*
Aileron, *122*
Air brake, 232–233
Airplane (*See* Flight, story of)
Alpha particles, 220
Alternating current, 140–141; *139*
Amber, 126
American Arithmometer Co., 231–232
Ampère, André, 133, 151
Amplification, *190*
Appert, Nicholas, 236
Arabic science, 27–28
Archimedes, 21, 22–24; *22, 23*
Aristotle, 21
Arithmetic, "invention" of, 21; Roman, 26–27
Arkwright, Richard, 246
Armat, Thomas, 86
Armato, Salvino D', 51
Aspdin, Joseph, 237
Astronomy, 35, 56–58
Atom, 183; atomic energy, 220–227; *223, 225, 226;* medical uses, 227; structure, *182*
Atomic bomb, 220, 222
Audiofrequency wave, 198; *199*
Audion tube, 187
Automobile, story of, 102–110; *104–109*

Bacon, Francis, 35
Bacteriology, 52
Balloon, 233; *233*
Bardeen, Dr. John, 255
Barium, 221
Barometer, 233–234; *234*
Battery, electric, 130–131; *131*
Beach, Alfred, 59; typewriter, *60*
Bell, Alexander Graham, 164–167, 170–172; *166–167, 168, 172, 173, 180, 181*
Bell, Alexander Melville, 171
Bell, electric, 217–218; *217*

Bell Laboratories, 215, 255–257
Berliner, Emile, 247, 251
Bernoulli's principle, 112–113, 122; *113*
Beryllium, 220, 221
Bessemer, Sir Henry, 254–255
Besson, 31
Bicycle, 234–236; *235*
Blenkinsop, John, 95; locomotive, *96*
Blériot, Louis, 117; plane, *119*
Bliss, George, 71
Bohr, Niels, 222
Bourseul, 171
Boyer, Joseph, 232
Brandenberger, Jacques F., 236
Brattain, Walter, 255
Bronze Age, 16
Buick, David, 103, 104
Bullet, Nicholas, 51
Burroughs, William Seward, 231–232

Cadillac, 106
Cadillac Automobile Co., 104
Cairo Museum, 19
Calculus, 22, 37, 262
Calotypes, 79
Camera, 75–82; *76, 77, 83*
Canning, 236, 262
Capacitor, 127; variable, 200–202; *200, 201*
Carey, G. R., 202–203
Carhart, Dr. J. W., steam car, *106*
Cartwright, Edmund, 246
Cassegrain telescope, 57; *56*
Cast iron, 31
Cathode beam, 204–208; *203, 205, 207*
Cavalieri, 23
Cayley, Sir George, 111–112
Cecil, W., 100–101
Cellophane, 236–237
Cement, 237
Chadwick, James, 220
Chain reaction, 224–225; *225*
Chanute, Octave, 113–114

Chapin, J. R., 253
Charch, Dr. Hale, 236
Charles' law, 110
Charles the Wise, King, 237
Cheops, King, 20
Chinese science, 27, 28
CinemaScope, 89, 90, 91
Cinerama, 89–91; *91*
Clock, 237–238; *237, 238*
Cloth, weaving of, 15, 262
Clothing, primitive, 15
Clymer, George, 45; press, *46*
Collodion, 79, 80
Colt, Samuel, 251–252
Columbia University, 222
Condensor, electrical, 127 (*See also* Capacitor)
Conductors, electrical, 126
Cooking, discovery of, 14
Coolidge, 244
Copernicus, 34–35
Copper, discovery of, 15–16
Corning Glass Works, 57
Coster, Janszoon, 38
Cotton gin, 238, 240; *239*
Coulomb's law, 189
Crank, principle of, 29, 31; *31*
Crankshaft, 101–102; *102*
Crompton, Samuel, 246
Cugnot, Nicholas Joseph, 93; steam tractor, *92*
Cummings, Alexander, 258
Curtiss, Glenn, 113, 118; biplane, *119*
Cushman, 171
Cyclotron, 223–224; *223*

Daguerre, Louis, 77, 78–79; daguerreotype method, 79, 80
Davy, Sir Humphry, 76–77, 134
Day, Prof. Jeremiah, 147, 151, 152
DC-7 airliner, *120*
De Forest, Lee, 21, 88, 187, 190–191, 193; *189;* vacuum tube, *188*
De Witt Clinton train, *96–97*
Democratic National Convention, 157
Densmore, James, 61–63
Diesel engine, 102, 110; *110–111*
Diode, 187; *183*
Direct current, *139*
Dissector tube, 204
Drais, Baron von, 234
Dry-plate process, 80
Du Pont de Nemours, E. I., 236
Dunlop, John Boyd, 236, 255
Duryea, Charles E., 101, 102–103; automobile, *105*
Duryea, J. Frank, 103
Dynamo, 137; *144*

Eastman, George, 80–82; *82*
Edison, Thomas Alva, 66; *184;* lamp, 183–184, 244; *188, 245;* microphone, 247; moving pic-
tures, 86; phonograph, 248, 251; *249–251;* teletype, 158; *156*
Edison Effect, 184–185; *186*
Egyptian science, 18–20
Einstein, Albert, 21, 192, 196, 220; equation, 222–223
Electric current, 183 (*See also* Alternating *and* Direct current)
Electricity, discovery of, 126–128, 130–131, 133 (*See also* applications, *e.g.,* Electromagnet, Generator, Vacuum tube, *etc.*)
Electromagnet, 145–147, 151, 153, 197–198, 262; *145, 185;* in bell, 217–218; *217;* in recording, 208, 210–211, 213–215; *211*
Electromagnetism, discovery of, 131, 133
Electromotive force, 138, 140, 144
Electrons, 183
Elevator, 240, 242; *241, 242*
Euclid, 21
Evans, Oliver, 93

Facsimile machine (*See* High-Speed Fax)
Faraday, Michael, 133, 134, 136–137, 195; *134*
Farnsworth, Philo, 204
Farrar, 171
Fermi, Enrico, 221, 222
Film, roll, 81–82
Fire, discovery of, 13–14
Fisher, George, 68, 69
Fisher Body Co., 106
Fleming, Sir John, 21, 185, 187; vacuum tube, *183*
Flight, story of, 110–114, 117–118, 121–125; early attempts, 113–114; *112–114;* improved planes, 117–118; *119;* jet and rocket propulsion, 123–125; *124;* principles of flight, 111, 112; *113, 114;* principle of plane, 118, 121–123; *121, 122;* Wrights, 114, 117; *115, 116*
Ford, Henry, 103, 106–107, 110
Fourdrinier process, 248
*Frankfurter Zeitung,* 40
Franklin, Benjamin, 127–128; *128*
Franklin Institute, 87
Fulton, Robert, 25

Gale, Leonard, 153
Galileo, 23, 34, 52, 238
Galvani, Luigi, 128, 130; *129*
Gas lighting, 242
Gasoline engine, 100–102; *101–103*
Gearwheel, invention of, 24, 27
General Motors Co., 104
Generator, electric, invention of, 133–134, 136–137; *135;* principle of, 138, 140–141; *135–137, 139*
Gilbert, Dr. William, 126; *127*
Glidden, Carlos, 59
Glider, 113–114, 117; *113, 114*
Goddard, John, 80
Goldschmidt, J., 234

Goodyear, Charles, 252–253
Gravitation, law of, 37
Gray, Elisha, 171
Gray, Stephen, 126
Greek science, 21–26
Greene, Nathanael, 240
Grew, Nehemiah, 52
Gutenberg, Johann, 38, 44
Gutenberg Bible, 40

Hahn, Otto, 221–222
Hale telescope, *57*
Half-tone process, 204, 242, 244; *205*
Hargraves, James, 246
Hartshorne, Stewart, 253
Harvester, 244; *243*
Haynes, Elwood, 103
Heavy water, 225
Heliography, 79
Helmholtz, Hermann von, 171, 197
Henry, Joseph, 145, 153, 158; *145*
Hero of Alexandria, 21, 24–26, 27; inventions, *24–25*
Hero, King, 23
Herring, 113–114; glider, *114*
Herschel, Sir John, 78–79
Hertz, Heinrich, 21, 192–193, 194, 195, 196–197; *195*
High-Speed Fax, 160, 164; *161*
Hill's gasoline buggy, *106*
Hiroshima, 222
Hoe, Robert, & Co., 46, 48, 49
Hooke, Dr. Robert, 52, 238
Horner, Dr. W. G., 83; movie device, *85*
*Horse in Motion, The,* 85
Howe, Elias, 67–69, 71, 74–75; *67;* sewing machine, *68*
Hunt, Walter, 66–67; 253; *66*
Hussey, Obed, 244
Huygens, Christian, 53, 238
Hydrogen bomb, 222, 262
Hyland, Lt., 252

Iconoscope, 204
Insulators, electrical, 126
Internal combustion engine, 100–125, 262
Inventions, fifteen greatest, 262
Iron, smelting of, 29, 31
Ives, Frederick Eugene, 242

Jackson, Dr., 151, 155–156
Jenkins, C. Francis, 86–87
Jet propulsion, 123–125; *123, 124*
Jewelry, first, 15
Judson, Whitcomb L., 261
Jupiter, 52

Kelly press, 50–51; *49–51*
Kettering, Charles F., 106
Kinetoscope, 86; *88*

Kitty Hawk, N.C., 117
Kleinsteuber's machine shop, 59, 61, 66; *59*
Kodak, 82; *83*
Koenig, Friedrich, 46–48
Krypton, 221

Lackawanna Railroad, 219
Lamp, incandescent, 184, 244; *188, 245*
Langley, Dr. Samuel P., 112–113, 117
Latham's plane, *119*
Lathe, 244
Lawrence, 223
Leeuwenhoek, Anton van, 52
Leibnitz, 22
Leland, Henry M., 104, 106
Lens, 51, 53–55; *53–55*
Leonardo da Vinci, 23, 31, 34, 111, 240; inventions, *34–37*
Lever, principle of, 16–17, 24, 262; *17*
Leyden jar, 127, 128; *127*
Light, nature of, 37, 53
Lilienthal, Otto, 113; glider, *114*
Lindbergh, Charles A., 117, 118; plane, *120*
Linotype, 42–44, 47; *39, 41–44*
Lippershey, Hans, 52
Lippincott, J. B., 85
Livingston, 223
Locomotive, 93–95, 98–99; *95–99*
Lodge, 21
London *Daily Mail,* 117
London *Times,* 47
Loom, 244, 246; *245*

McCormick, Cyrus, 244; *243*
Machinery, principles of, 24
Maddox, Richard, 80
Magee, 236
Magnetic tape recording (*See* Sound recording)
Magnetism, 126, 131, 212 (*See also* Electromagnetism)
Malpighi, Marcello, 52
Manly, G. H., 113
Manzetti, 171
Marcellus, 23
Marconi, 21, 193, 195
Match, 246–247
Mathematics, Egyptian, 18; Greek, 21, 22–23; Roman, 26–27; *27*
Maudslay, Henry, 244
Maxwell, James Clerk, 21, 194–196, 197; *195*
Medical uses of atomic energy, 227
Meitner, Lise, 221
Mergenthaler, Ottmar, 42, 47; *39, 40*
Metal, smelting of, 15–16, 262
Meucci, 171
Michaux, Ernst, 235
Microphone, 171, 247; *246*
Microscope, 51–53, 55, 262; *55*
Middle Ages, 28, 29–31

Milky Way, 58
Mill, Henry, 61
Model T Ford, 107
Mongolfier, Joseph and Etienne, 233
Monotype, 43
Morse, Samuel F. B., 147–158; *146*
Morse telegraphic code, *152*
Motor, electric, 141, 143–145; *142, 143*
Mt. Wilson Observatory, 58
Moving pictures, 82–91; CinemaScope and Cinerama, 89–91; *91;* early movies, 82–83; *84–86;* first projector, 86–87; *87;* Kinetograph, *86;* kinetoscope, 86, *88;* Muybridge motion studies, 85–86; sound recording, 215–216; *212;* Vitascope, 87–88; *89*
Murdoch, William, 242
Murphy, Edward R., 104
Muybridge, Eadweard, 85–86

Napoleon, 131
Neff, C. A., 258
Negative, photographic, 77–78
Neutrons, 183, 220–221, 223
New York *Times,* 40
New York *Tribune,* 42, 48; *41*
Newcomen, Thomas, 91, 92
Newspapers (*See* Printing)
Newton, Sir Isaac, 22, 23, 35, 37, 53; his third law, 123–124
Newtonian telescope, 56–57; *56*
Niepce, Joseph N., 77–78
Nile river, 18, 20
Nineveh, 51
Nipkow, Dr. Paul, 203
Nuclear fission, 222
Nuclear reactor, 224–225, 227; *226*

Oakland Motor Co., 104
Oersted, Hans Christian, 131–132, 141, 158; *133*
Olds, R. E., 103, 104
Oldsmobile, 103; *105*
Optics, story of, 51–58; first lenses, 51; how lens works, 53–55; *53–54;* microscope, 51–53; *55;* reflector telescopes, 56–58; *56–58;* telescope invented, 52
Otis, Elisha G., 240

Palomar telescope, 57–58; *57, 58*
Pan American Airways, 118
Paper, invention of, 28
Paper, mass production of, 247–248; *246–247*
Papyrus, 17
Parabolic mirror, 58; *58*
Parchment, 17
Paris Exposition, 214
Pascal, 23
Penaud's model plane, *112*
Pennsylvania Railroad, 232

Pentode tube, 181; *187*
Pertzel, 80
Petrina, 171
Phantascope, 87
Phelps, 75
Phenakistoscope, 83; *85*
Philadelphia *Ledger,* 48
Phillips, A. D., 247
Phonograph, 248, 251; *249–251*
Photoelectric cell, 88, 160, 164, 188–189, 216; *194, 212, 214*
Photoelectric tube, 191–194; *194*
Photography, story of, 75–91; daguerreotype, 78–80; *78;* early, 75–78; *76–77;* Eastman's improvements, 81–82; *83;* half-tone process, 204, 242, 244; *205;* "pictures sent through space," 216–217; *214 (See also* Moving pictures)
Pistol, 251–252; *252* •
Pistons in gas engine, 101–102; *101–103*
Planck's Constant, 193
Plateau, Dr. Joseph, 82–83; movie device, *84*
Plato, 21
Pogin, M., 61
Polaroid glass, 90
Polk, James K., 157
Pope, 236
Pottery, 14
Poulsen, Valdemar, 213–214
Press, printing, early, 44–48; *45–47;* modern, 48–51; *48–51*
Primitive man, 13–17
*Principia,* Newton's, 37
Printing, story of, 38–51; early presses, 44–48; *45–47;* first newspaper, 40; Linotype, 42–44; *39, 41–44;* modern press, 48–51; *48–51;* movable type, 38, 40, 262
Projecting lantern, 55; *55*
Propeller, airplane, 121; *121*
Protons, 183, 220
Pulley, 22, 24
Pump, Hero's, 24, 25; *24*
Pyramids, building of, 19–20; *20*
Pythagoras, 21–22

Quincy Hall Clothing Mfg. Co., 69

Radar, 252
Radcliff, William, 246
Radio, 170–171, 194–202; Hertz's discoveries, 196–197; *196;* how radio works, 198–202; Maxwell's theory, 195–196; waves explained, 197–200; *199 (See also* Vacuum tube *and* Television)
Radio Corporation of America, 204, 252
Radioisotopes, 227
Radium, 220, 221
Ramelli, 31, 34; inventions, *32–33*
Reaumur, René de, 248

Rectifier, 181, 183, 187; *183*
Reflector vs. refractor telescope, 56–57
Reichenbach, Henry, 82
Reid, Whitelaw, *39*
Reis, Philipp, 171
Relativity, theory of (*See* Einstein)
Remington typewriter, 63; *65*
Renaissance, 28, 31
Resonator, 197; *196*
Revolver, 251–252; *252*
Riebau's shop, 133
Robert, Louis, 247–248
Rocket propulsion, 123–125
Roentgen, Prof. W. K., 260
Rogers, Thomas, locomotive, *97*
Roget, Dr. Peter, 82–83
Roman science, 26–27
Roosevelt, President, 222
Rubber, 252–253
Rust, Samuel, 45
Rutherford, Ernest, 220

Safety pin, 253; *253*
Saturn, 52
Sauria, Dr. Charles, 247
Savery, Thomas, 91–92
Scanning disc, 203
Schwalbach, 59
*Scientific American,* 59, 254–255
Screw, 22, 24, 262; Archimedes', *23*
Self-starter, 106
Sennett, Mack, 88
Sewing machine, 66–75; *68, 70, 72–75*
Sheele, Karl William, 76
Shockley, Dr. William, 256
Sholes, Christopher Latham, 59, 61–63, 66; *59*
Singer, Isaac Merritt, 71–75; *71*
Siphon, Hero's, 24, 25; *25;* in toilet, 258, 260; *258*
Smith, David Eugene, 22–23
Smith, Uriah, horseless carriage, *104*
Smith press, *45*
Smithsonian Institution, 103, 112, 145
Sound recording, 208, 210; electrical transcriptions, 210–212; *211, 213;* sound for movies, 215–216; *213;* tape and wire recording, 212, 214–215; *213*
Soule, Samuel, 59
Spectacles, 51–52
Stanford, Leland, 85
Stanhope press, *46*
Static electricity, 128
Steam engine, 24, 25, 91–99, 112; *25, 92–98*
Steel, Bessemer process, 254–255
Stephenson, George, 95, 98
Sterns, J. B., 157
Stock ticker, 158
Stockton & Darlington Railway, 95, 98
Stone Age, 16

Strassman, F., 221, 222
Sturgeon, William, 145
"Sully," 151; *148*
Sundback, Gideon, 261
Switchboard, first, *169*

Talbot, William H. F., 79
Talbotypes, 79
Talon Hookless Fastener Co., 261
Technicolor, 88, 89
Telegraph, 147–164; first message, 156; improvements, 157–158; modern, 159–160, 164; *161–163;* Morse invents, 147–157; *147–153* (*See also* Teletype)
Telephone, 146, 164–181; Bell invents, 164–165, 170–172; *166–168, 172–173, 180–181;* dial system, 173, 178–181; *176–179;* how phone works, 172–173; *170, 174–175;* other inventors, 171
Telescope, 51–52, 53, 56–58; *56–58*
Teletype, 146, 158–160; *155–157, 163*
Television, 202–208; *203, 205, 207, 209*
Tesla, 21
Thomas, 69
Thomson, Sir J. J., 185
Three-D movies, 90–91
Three-finger rule, 138; *137*
Thurber, Charles, 61; typewriter, *60*
Tire, pneumatic, 255
Toilet (*See* Water closet)
Torricelli, 233–234
Transistor, 255–257; *255*
Trevithick, Richard, 93–95
Triode, 187; *186*
Twain, Mark, letter, 66; *64*
Type, movable, 38, 40, 262
Typewriter, 59–66; *59–65*

Uchatius, Baron Franz von, 83
Underwood typewriter, 66; *65*
Uranium, 221–222, 224

Vacuum tube, 88, 181, 183–194, 262; Edison Effect, 184–185; *186;* how it works, 181, 183; *185;* photoelectric tube, 191–194; *194;* principle of tube, 189–191; *190–192;* radio tube, 187; *188*
Vail, Alfred, 154–157
Varley, 171
Velayer, 240
Vick, Henry de, 237–238
Vidi, M., 234
Vitascope, 87–88; *89*
Volta, Alessandro, 130–131; *130*
Voltaic cell, 131; *131*
Vulcanizing process, 253

Walker, John, 246–247
Water clock, 24

Water closet, 257–258, 260; *257–259*
Water mill, 29; *30*
Water wheel, 27
Watson, Thomas A., 165, 170
Watt, James, 92–93, 112
Weapons, cave man's, 13
Weaving (*See* Cloth)
Wedge, principle of, 24, 262
Wedgewood, Thomas, 76–77
Weller, Charlie, 61
Western Union Telegraph Co., 157, 160
Westinghouse, George, 232
Wet-plate process, 80; *81*
Wheel, 16, 24, 262; *19*
Whitney, Eli, 238, 240; *239*
Whittle, Air Commodore Frank A., 124
Windmill, 27
Window-shade roller, 253

Winton, Alexander, 103
Wright, Orville and Wilbur, 101, 114, 117; patent, *116;* planes, *115*
Wright, Senator Silas, 157
Writing, art of, 17, 262
Wyckoff, Seamans & Benedict, 66

X-ray tube, 260–261

Yeates, 171
Yerkes Observatory, 56
Yost, 63

Zieber, 75
Zipper, 261
Zoetrope, 83
Zonca, 31
Zworykin, Dr. Vladimir Kosma, 203–204

## About the Author

JEROME S. MEYER has written over two dozen books, many of which have been best sellers.

Born and educated in New York City, Mr. Meyer studied engineering at Columbia University, leaving to serve in the First World War. In 1925 he joined the staff of an advertising agency, two years later setting up his own agency. His first two books were published in that same year.

Mr. Meyer is responsible for the first radio quiz program. Among his books are *Picture Book of the Weather, Fun for the Family, Mind Your P's and Q's, The Book of Amazing Facts, Fun with Mathematics,* etc. He has also done many feature articles for many popular magazines.